INDIANS

POCAHONTAS, *Seymour*
SACAGAWEA, *Seymour*
SEQUOYAH, *Snow*
SITTING BULL, *Stevenson*
SQUANTO, *Stevenson*
TECUMSEH, *Stevenson*

NAVAL HEROES

DAVID FARRAGUT, *Long*
GEORGE DEWEY, *Long*
JOHN PAUL JONES, *Snow*
MATTHEW CALBRAITH PERRY, *Scharbach*
OLIVER HAZARD PERRY, *Long*
RAPHAEL SEMMES, *Snow*
STEPHEN DECATUR, *Smith*

NOTED WIVES and MOTHERS

ABIGAIL ADAMS, *Wagoner*
DOLLY MADISON, *Monsell*
JESSIE FREMONT, *Wagoner*
MARTHA WASHINGTON, *Wagoner*
MARY TODD LINCOLN, *Wilkie*
NANCY HANKS, *Stevenson*
RACHEL JACKSON, *Govan*

SCIENTISTS and INVENTORS

ALBERT EINSTEIN, *Hammontree*
ALECK BELL, *Widdemer*
CYRUS MCCORMICK, *Dobler*
ELI WHITNEY, *Snow*
ELIAS HOWE, *Corcoran*
ELIZABETH BLACKWELL, *Henry*
GEORGE CARVER, *Stevenson*
GEORGE EASTMAN, *Henry*
HENRY FORD, *Aird and Ruddiman*
JOHN AUDUBON, *Mason*
LUTHER BURBANK, *Burt*
MARIA MITCHELL, *Melin*
ROBERT FULTON, *Henry*
SAMUEL MORSE, *Snow*
TOM EDISON, *Guthridge*
WALTER REED, *Higgins*
WILBUR AND ORVILLE WRIGHT, *Stevenson*
WILL AND CHARLIE MAYO, *Hammontree*

SOCIAL and CIVIC LEADERS

BETSY ROSS, *Weil*
BOOKER T. WASHINGTON, *Stevenson*
CLARA BARTON, *Stevenson*
DAN BEARD, *Mason*
FRANCES WILLARD, *Mason*
JANE ADDAMS, *Wagoner*
J. STERLING MORTON, *Moore*
JULIA WARD HOWE, *Wagoner*
JULIETTE LOW, *Higgins*
LILIUOKALANI, *Newman*
LUCRETIA MOTT, *Burnett*
MOLLY PITCHER, *Stevenson*
OLIVER WENDELL HOLMES, JR., *Dunham*
SUSAN ANTHONY, *Monsell*

SOLDIERS

ANTHONY WAYNE, *Stevenson*
BEDFORD FORREST, *Parks*
DAN MORGAN, *Bryant*
ETHAN ALLEN, *Winders*
FRANCIS MARION, *Steele*
ISRAEL PUTNAM, *Stevenson*
JEB STUART, *Winders*
NATHANAEL GREENE, *Peckham*
ROBERT E. LEE, *Monsell*
SAM HOUSTON, *Stevenson*
TOM JACKSON, *Monsell*
U. S. GRANT, *Stevenson*
WILLIAM HENRY HARRISON, *Peckham*
ZACK TAYLOR, *Wilkie*

JEFF DAVIS, *and Delaune*
JOHN MARSHALL, *Monsell*
TEDDY ROOSEVELT, *Parks*
WOODROW WILSON, *Monsell*

Washington Irving

Boy of Old New York

Illustrated by Gray Morrow

Washington Irving

Boy of Old New York

By Mabel Cleland Widdemer

THE **BOBBS-MERRILL** COMPANY, INC.
A SUBSIDIARY OF HOWARD W. SAMS & CO., INC.
Publishers · INDIANAPOLIS · NEW YORK

For my son John
with love

Illustrations

Contents

Books by Mabel Cleland Widdemer

ALECK BELL: INGENIOUS BOY
DE WITT CLINTON: BOY BUILDER
HARRIET BEECHER STOWE: CONNECTICUT GIRL
JAMES MONROE: GOOD NEIGHBOR BOY
PETER STUYVESANT: BOY WITH WOODEN SHOES
WASHINGTON IRVING: BOY OF OLD NEW YORK

★ ★ Washington Irving

Boy of Old New York

A Boy Named Washington

IT WAS early morning of a late September day in 1787 and the pleasant top-floor room of the white house on William Street, on the tip end of Manhattan Island, was flooded with sunshine. A boy, asleep in a small trundle bed, turned and buried his blond head under the heavy hand-knit blanket to shut out the annoying light.

Except for a large black cat, curled up on the patchwork quilt at his feet, the boy was alone. The big four-posted bed where two of his elder brothers, Ebenezer and John, slept, was empty. They had dressed an hour ago and gone down to their breakfast.

The door opened and the boys' mother approached the bed quietly. Her brown eyes softened as she looked down at her youngest son, so sound asleep. It seemed to her that it was only yesterday that he had been a baby. Now he was four and a half years old and starting to school this morning.

She bent and kissed him and he opened his gray eyes and stared at her for a long moment. She had awakened him from a lovely dream. He was very sleepy, but he knew something wonderful was going to happen to him this morning. But what was it?

"Is it Christmas?" he asked. But his mother shook her pretty head.

"No. That comes when it is cold and there is snow on the ground and sleigh bells ring and we put crumbs out for the birds. The Hudson River is frozen over then and the ice has to be broken in the public wells."

"Sometimes there is ice in the pitchers on our washstands, too," Washington said. He thought for a moment.

"My birthday!" he squealed, but she shook her head again and smiled.

"That comes on April third when the tulips and daffodils dance in the spring sunshine. This is autumn. See the maple tree outside your window! Yesterday when the wind blew hard you said its leaves fell around you like red rain. Try again. Surely you haven't forgotten what is special about this day."

Then suddenly he remembered.

He sat up in bed and threw his arms around his mother's neck.

"I know! I'm going to school and learn to read and write! Then I'll never have to ask anyone to read aloud to me again. And I can write down all the thoughts that pop into my head, too. I've wanted to read and write so long."

His mother hugged and kissed him. "So you are! Now hop out of bed and dress, or you will be late. Sarah is already waiting for you at the breakfast table. She is very proud to be taking her young brother to Mrs. Kilmaster's school."

The boy threw back the blankets and swung his thin legs over the side of the low bed. He tested the floor with one bare toe. It was cold. The new suit his mother had made for him from a topcoat that belonged to his father hung over the back of a chair. The boy looked at it with proud eyes.

"Tell me a story, Mother," he begged. "It will help me to dress faster. I'll listen to the story and dress at the same time."

"Very well." Mrs. Irving went over and began to plump up the feather-stuffed pillows on the four-poster bed and smooth out the rumpled blankets she had knit. "What would you like to hear?" she asked.

14

The boy thought for a long moment. Then he said, "Tell me why you and Father named me Washington. It's a terribly big name for me."

"So it is," she laughed. "It belongs to a big man, General George Washington. He fought to free this country and give us back our rightful happiness. He is a good, brave man, and you should be proud to bear his name."

"But Washington is his last name and my first!" The little boy was puzzled. He had often wondered why his parents hadn't called him a nice name like John or Peter or William. His brothers all had names like those. But Washington was a man's name and a man's last name at that!

His mother smiled as she patted the heavy, handmade, white counterpane into place.

"I'll start from the beginning, as you always ask me to do," she said. "We Irvings are a very large family, I am happy to say. There's your father and I, then the children, William, Ann, Peter, Catherine, Ebenezer, John, and Sarah . . . So when you came along we had pretty well run out of ordinary names. I thought it would be nice to name you after General George Washington, who has done so much for his country. The more we said the name over, Washington Irving, the better we liked it."

16

The boy was struggling into the long tight blue trousers, the first he had ever owned, so he was a trifle breathless and could only nod his head. When he could speak again he said, "I like my name now and I am glad you called me Washington after a brave general."

"Try to live up to it, dear," Mrs. Irving said gently. She crossed the room to tie the soft black bow under the broad ruffled collar of his new cambric shirt. She had sat up the night before and finished the shirt by candlelight for her youngest son's first day at school.

The First Day at School

WHEN BREAKFAST was over Mrs. Irving walked down to the garden gate with her two younger children, Sarah and Washington, who were eager to be off.

Washington walked slowly and stiffly for he was not used to his new suit. His mother looked at him and smiled.

"Come, dear!" she said. "You don't have to feel uneasy. There will be other boys in new suits at the school. I made it for you to enjoy. I want you to be happy and have fun while you are wearing it."

Washington drew a sigh of relief.

18

"Good-by, my darlings," Mrs. Irving said as she kissed her children.

The long street was wide and sunny and lined on each side by houses owned by Dutch families. Some of the houses were whitewashed; others were of yellow brick. Many of the roofs were high-peaked with gable ends. Almost every house was topped by a black or gilded iron weathercock that whirled and twirled in the breezes from the Hudson River. The children were so excited that they hopped and skipped the whole length of the street. They refused to listen to Lizzie, their faithful Scotch nurse, who begged them to walk quietly like a little lady and gentleman. But who wanted to walk slowly on a sharp September morning when the wind from the west whistled gay tunes and the red and yellow leaves danced madly? Poor distracted Lizzie was relieved when they turned the corner into Anne Street, where she could leave them.

There before them was Mrs. Kilmaster's small white clapboard house with its bright blue shutters. The Irving children ran up to the blue door with its shining brass knocker in the shape of a man's smiling face. Washington could just reach it when he stood on tiptoe.

Rat-a-tat-tat went the knocker. The door was opened at once by a pleasant-faced woman. She wore a white frilled cap and a black woolen dress with a tight waist and a long full skirt. She smiled when she saw Washington's eager face and held out her hand.

"Washington Irving, I am very glad to have you in my school," she said.

"I'm glad to come," the little boy answered. His frank gray eyes were shining. "I want to learn to read and write. Then I can read storybooks all day long if I want to."

"You must learn arithmetic, too," Mrs. Kilmaster told him.

20

Washington shook his blond head. "Sarah can do that," he answered. But Sarah shook her brown head and made a little face. She didn't like arithmetic either.

Suddenly everyone was startled by a very loud "Miaow!" Gussie, the Irving's big black cat, had followed the children to school. Now she marched up the gravel path, her long, thin, black tail waving, her green eyes fixed on Mrs. Kilmaster's kind face.

"Miaow!" she said again.

"Gussie is asking you if she may come to your school, too!" Washington laughed.

"I know Gussie very well. Sometimes she comes around and catches my mice. Come in, Gussie," Mrs. Kilmaster said. She stepped aside so the children and the cat might enter.

In a corner of the sunny hall there was a great brass cage and inside the cage was a green feathered parrot.

Mrs. Kilmaster's brother had brought the parrot to her from half across the world. Her brother was the captain of a sailing ship that touched many ports. Mrs. Kilmaster was very proud of the present he had given her.

Washington ran to the cage. He had never seen a parrot before. He thought the bird was wonderful when it said, "Good morning," to him. He didn't want to leave it.

But Mrs. Kilmaster took his hand and drew him into the sunny schoolroom. "Mike will be there at recess," she promised.

Gussie didn't have to go into the schoolroom. She stayed out in the hall with Mike. She sat down under his brass cage and stared at him with her round green eyes. She was still staring at him when school was dismissed at noon.

Washington ran to Mike's cage. "Good morning," he said.

"Good morning," Mike answered.

"My name is Washington," the little boy said.

"Washington," Mike repeated turning his head from one side to another. Suddenly he put up his claw and saluted. Mrs. Kilmaster had taught him always to salute when he heard General George Washington's name.

"I am going to stay out here in the hall and talk to it," Washington said.

Gussie got up and stretched. Then she made deep noises in her throat. Mike stared down at her. He didn't like cats.

"You can scare Gussie just by saying, 'scat, scat, you bad black cat,' " he said laughing. But it was too much for Mike to learn in a day.

"You must give him time," Mrs. Kilmaster said. "He'll learn it after a while. He is a very clever parrot."

Mike almost scared the children and Gussie out of their skins! He suddenly shouted, "Bad cat! Bad cat!" and he scowled at her.

Gussie slunk under a chair. Washington looked at Mike admiringly. Then, his eyes twinkling, he turned to Mrs. Kilmaster.

"I don't think Mike's a bird at all," he said. "I think he's a little man dressed in green feathers. No bird could be that smart. I'm going to like school even better than I thought I would."

London Bridge

WASHINGTON IRVING liked Mrs. Kilmaster's school. He liked the big sunny schoolroom and the other boys and girls. He was friendly and he liked people, so people liked him too. He enjoyed learning to read, and he found arithmetic wasn't too hard, either.

When the children went out to play games in the deep old garden back of Mrs. Kilmaster's house, Washington's sister Sarah suggested they play London Bridge.

"You'd better let Washington be one side of the bridge," Sarah said.

"Why?" the children wanted to know.

"We always let him be one side of the bridge when we play at home. He thinks up fine things for us to choose from. Everyone always wants to be on his side," Sarah explained.

"But he is the youngest child in the school," the others said. When they saw how disappointed Sarah was they added, "We'll let him be one side today because it's his first day at school."

"London Bridge is falling down,
Falling down, falling down,
London Bridge is falling down,
My fair lady!"

sang the children.

The first to be caught was a boy of ten. He was so tall he could scarcely get under the bridge, half of which was made by Washington's short arms. He made all the children laugh by crawling through the small space.

Milly Jones, who was twelve and the oldest pupil in the school, was the other half.

"Which would you like best," she asked importantly, as they held the ten-year-old boy between them, "a sack of sugarplums or—?" She looked at Washington. "It's your turn," she said.

"Or a great white horse, all shining in the sunlight and dancing and prancing to the music of a parade!" Washington said. He looked very funny, for he had shut his eyes and screwed up his face, the better to see in his mind the horse he was describing.

"Oh, the horse! Who cares about sugarplums when he can have a prancing horse!"

So the big boy got behind Washington and put his arms around his waist. The game went on. When all the children had been "caught" most of them were in line behind Washington Irving, each holding on to the boy or girl in front of him. Only a few greedy ones preferred the sugarplums to the horse that danced in the sunlight to the music of a parade.

Then Milly tightened her grip on Washington's hands. All the children behind them hung on tight. Milly's side pulled one way in a tug of war and Washington's side pulled the other way. Washington and his large group were by far the stronger.

Washington's side of the bridge easily pulled the other side across the dry grass and they all fell into a laughing heap.

Mrs. Kilmaster came out to see what the fun was about. When they told her she smiled and nodded and seated herself on a stone bench.

"Washington has imagination," she said.

"What's imagination?" Washington asked.

"It's something inside of you that paints pictures on your mind," Mrs. Kilmaster explained. "You have a great deal of it."

Following His Nose

THE BROWN earth in the Irving's garden was warm from the April sun. Tiny green shoots of flowers and grass were pressing up through it. Spring had come late that year and there were no daffodils or tulips. Only a few pale snowdrops lifted their little heads.

Washington Irving stood on the crosspiece of the white picket gate and swung slowly back and forth. It was his birthday. He was five and he felt very much older than he had the day before!

To begin with, he was going to have a birthday party. It was the first real one he had ever had, and he had been looking forward to it.

There would be two other boys and three girls and all his brothers and sisters. Of course his parents would be there too. He was proud because he was going to have such a big party.

His mother had sent him out to play while she baked the birthday cake for him. Lizzie was baking too. She was making bread and the delicious Scotch biscuits, called scones, for which she was famous. It smelled nice in the kitchen, but it smelled nice out here, too, of fresh-turned earth and green things growing.

Suddenly he was conscious of a new and more delicious smell. It was the sea, but Washington didn't know that. Perhaps because he had been used to it all his life, he hadn't noticed it before. But certainly there was something different about it today. All at once the yard, where he usually enjoyed playing, seemed cramped.

"I wonder where it comes from?" he thought. "I wish I knew."

30

Then he remembered that his mother had always told him to follow his nose if he wanted to find something. He jumped off the gate. Sniffing deeply, he followed his short nose out of the garden and through the gate and into the sunshine of William Street.

The delicious smell grew stronger. He turned into Broad Way and here he lost it for a minute or two as three fat old pigs waddled toward him. They were grunting. They sounded angry. Washington began backing away from them.

"Stop!" he shouted at them. "You're big bad pigs! Go away!" He picked up a stick to throw at them. "You get away from me!"

That made the oldest, ugliest pig angrier. It lowered its head and rushed at Washington and toppled him flat on his back into the dust of the roadway. Then the pig stopped.

Washington sat up. The old pig stood over him, but Washington wasn't afraid.

"Go away, you nasty old ham and bacon!" he shouted. "I'll hit you with this stick if you don't go away!"

A cheerful voice said, "Wait a minute, fellow!" Washington saw a big boy bending over him and holding out a friendly, strong, brown hand. The pigs were walking slowly away.

"What did you call that old pig?" Washington's new friend was laughing as he pulled the boy to his feet and dusted him off as well as he could with a big red cotton handkerchief.

"Bacon and ham. And that's all he is," Washington answered stoutly.

The big boy laughed harder than ever. "That's a good one!" he said. "But don't you know you mustn't shake a stick at a pig? Pigs don't like that. It makes them angry. Suppose I walk home with you and keep the pigs away."

With the pigs gone the delicious smell came back and Washington began to sniff again.

32

"No, thank you," he said politely. "I'm trying to find where that nice smell comes from. My mother told me if I wanted to find something I should follow my nose." He sniffed again.

His new friend drew in two deep breaths and said, "That's the smell of the sea. It comes from the Battery. Would you like to walk down and take a look?"

They walked down Broad Way together. The spring sun fell gently on their bare heads. It fell gently on the many houses built in the Dutch style, with gables facing the street. The roofs of the houses were shaped like steps. These steps made comfortable places for birds to light on.

"What is your name?" Washington asked the big boy. "Mine is Washington Irving."

"I am Peter Gaansvoot. My mother and father were Dutch, but I am an American. I was born in this country. When my parents were alive we lived in a house on the Bowery."

As the big boy and the small boy walked on down the street, Peter continued, "The Bowery is a nice place to live. It's just a dusty country road, but the houses are all built in the good Dutch way like that one yonder. They have nice gardens all around them, and lots of folks have apple orchards, too."

Washington looked up into Peter's kind, round Dutch face. "I like Dutch people," he said. "I wish I were Dutch, but Lizzie, my nurse, says I'm Scotch like her."

"I like Scotch people." Peter smiled.

They passed Trinity Church with its tall white steeple that seemed to little Washington to touch the blue sky. They went into the quiet church-yard to rest awhile. Washington tried out the alphabet he had learned at Mrs. Kilmaster's school and spelled some of the old names on the tombstones. Peter thought Washington was very clever to know all the letters.

Then they wandered down Wall Street to look at Federal Hall. Peter told Washington that the building used to be called City Hall. It had had to be enlarged when New York became the capital of their new country. Now laws which concerned the whole nation were passed there.

Next they went to Bowling Green. Peter pointed out the place where the Dutch had built Fort Amsterdam in 1626, when they had first landed on Manhattan Island. Then the boys crossed to the tiny patch of green called Bowling Green Park and leaned on the iron fence.

"This fence has a funny top," Washington said, running his hand over the rough iron posts.

Peter nodded. "Before the Revolution," he explained, "there used to be heads of the English royal family—like statues, you know—on top of these posts. But they were knocked off by the Americans to be made into bullets to help win the war. That is why they are so rough now."

"Look!" Washington exclaimed. "Those four old men are playing a game. What is it?"

Peter looked at the four old men in their tall, old-fashioned, sugar-loaf hats and smiled.

"They are playing a game of bowls," he said. "That's why this park is called the Bowling Green. It's an old game brought to this country by the crew of Captain Henry Hudson's ship when he discovered the Hudson River. Those wooden things at the end of the alley, which they are trying to knock down with the wooden balls, are called ninepins."

They watched for a while. The old men played quietly, not paying any attention to the boys leaning against the iron railing. Only the click of the wooden balls striking the ninepins broke the silence of the spring afternoon.

The smell was even more delicious when Washington and Peter crossed to Battery Park. Washington breathed deeply.

Peter caught Washington's hand. "Close your eyes and keep them closed until I tell you to open them. I will give you a great surprise," he said.

Washington obeyed and Peter led him to the low sea wall.

"Now!" cried Peter.

Washington opened his eyes and saw the water of New York Bay lying at his feet and stretching far into the distance. Lovely green islands dotted the blue water. Sea gulls flew through sunlight that silvered the tips of their wings, and then they rested on the waves.

"Oh," he cried, "no wonder it smells so good! It's so beautiful. And listen to the cries of those sea gulls!"

Then a tall-masted ship, with all her sails unfurled, came up the harbor. Washington thought it looked like a great white bird.

"I am going to sail all around the world in a ship like that!" he announced to Peter.

"So am I!" Peter answered and laughed. He added, "I start tomorrow on the 'Jolly Mate' as a cabin boy."

Washington looked in awe at his new friend. He suddenly felt very young. Then he remembered it was his fifth birthday and he was going to have a party. Probably at this very minute his mother was taking his birthday cake out of the oven and was getting ready to ice it in pink and put on the white candles.

"You must come home with me and eat some of my cake!" he told Peter Gaansvoot.

"I'd be glad to," Peter accepted gladly. "It's been a long time since I've seen a real home. I told you I was an orphan."

"What made you want to be a sailor?" Washington asked as they turned back toward William Street. "Have you always loved ships? Have you wanted to sail around the world for a long time? Would you like to be a sea captain?"

"The fireplace in our house on the Bowery had rough Dutch tiles all around it," Peter explained. "On long winter evenings I used to sit on the small three-legged stool that my father had made for me, and study the pictures on the tiles. My mother knew a story for each one of them. I don't know whether they were true or whether she made them up. Anyway, my favorite was about a big sailing ship. That tile had the nicest story of all. From the time I was your age I told myself I was going to sail around the world on a ship just like the one on the tile."

Washington decided that Peter was the nicest boy he knew. He was glad Peter was coming to the birthday party. He brought Peter into the house to meet his family. Peter thought it would be wonderful to have brothers and sisters.

The Irvings were happy to meet Washington's new friend. They made him feel welcome. Mrs. Irving was grateful for his being so kind to her youngest son. She put Peter next to her at the table and made sure he had the largest piece of cake. When it was time for him to return to his lodgings on the water front, she gave him her blessing and told him he must always remember the Irvings were his friends. She gave him a small packet made of red flannel and hemmed in black silk. There were needles and pins and black and white thread in it.

"Buttons have a way of popping off." She smiled. "And on shipboard there won't be a woman to sew them on for you. You'll have to learn to do your own mending."

"I'll never forget you," Peter promised. "I'll come back to see you someday."

President
George
Washington

WILLIAM IRVING, the oldest of all the Irving children, gave his youngest brother Washington a ship with white sails for his sixth birthday. The boy thought it was the most beautiful thing he had ever seen and he named it the "Freedom." Some day, he thought, he would sail around the world in a ship like the "Freedom."

It wasn't surprising that he should call his little boat the "Freedom," for he heard this word on everyone's lips these days.

New York was preparing to welcome General George Washington, who had fought for and won the freedom of the United States.

The people of America wanted him to be their President. They said, "He is the father of our new country. It should be guided by his wise head and hand." So they elected him the first President of the United States of America. He was arriving to make his home in the city on Cherry Street, and to gather around him other wise men who would help him govern.

Broad Way was gay with the new flag of the new country. The thirteen red and white stripes and the blue field with its thirteen silver stars fluttered from every window and balcony. Everyone put on his best holiday attire. And all faces shone with happiness and faith and hope.

Washington Irving was sailing his little boat in the horse trough, just outside the garden gate. He was imagining that the "Freedom" was the sailing ship on which Peter was a cabin boy. Just then William came to take his youngest brother along to see the sights.

Washington could scarcely believe his ears. All the Irving children liked to have William notice them. He was the oldest of them all and the most looked up to. He was only home on a visit. When his sister Ann had married Richard Dodge, William had gone with her to live on the Mohawk River, about forty miles north of Albany. Indians still roamed and hunted in that part of the country.

Washington rushed into the house to put away his boat and wash his face and hands. When he came out they started toward Broad Way. Washington had to half-run, half-walk to keep up with his tall brother's long stride. He soon grew breathless, but he wouldn't admit it and ask his brother to slow down. His curiosity got the better of him after a while and he panted, "What does the flag stand for, William?"

William looked down into the small red face and slackened his pace.

A street peddler, carrying a hand-woven basket of tiny flags, hurried up. "Buy your country's flag for a penny!" he cried. "Only a penny! Buy your country's flag!"

William reached into his pocket for a big copper penny and the man handed him a tiny flag.

"Here you are, Washington," William said and gave it to his young brother.

"What does the flag stand for?" Washington repeated after he had thanked William. He thought the tiny silk square was the most beautiful thing he had ever seen.

"Its blue is for justice," William explained gravely. "Its white is for purity of word and deed. Its red is the red lifeblood of brave men and women who stand ready to die or live worthily for their country. Its thirteen stars and stripes stand for the thirteen colonies."

"Has any other country a flag like ours?" young Washington Irving wanted to know.

"Every country has a flag, but none like ours. I have heard that General Washington himself drew the design when he was in Philadelphia in June, 1776."

The two brothers found a good place in the window of a barbershop to see the coming parade. The shop was on the second floor of a house near Fulton Street.

The barber's name was Coxe. He was a small man with moist eyes and a jumpy manner. He hurried to greet the brothers, for their father was a good customer. He placed chairs in the window for them so they could be comfortable while they watched the parade.

But six-year-old Washington soon grew tired of waiting. Someone rushed in with the news that the President was only now landing at the foot of Wall Street from his beautiful flower-decked barge. It would be another hour before the parade would start.

"I'm tired of sitting still, William," Washington whispered. "I've seen all the flags and decorations around here. I want to go somewhere else and see something new."

But William didn't want to leave the barbershop. He had met a friend, James Paulding, and his friend's sister. The sister was a very pretty girl with flashing dark eyes. She had dimples and curling brown hair. William thought she was charming and he wanted to stay and talk to her. He leaned from the window and spied Scotch Lizzie in the crowd below.

"Lizzie! Lizzie!" he called. "I've got Washington here with me. He says he's tired and wants to go somewhere else. Can he go with you? He wants to be in the crowd."

Lizzie's plain face lighted up. She was very fond of Washington and it seemed twice as nice to see things in his company.

"Tell him to come down," she called.

Washington rushed gladly down the steep stairs and out into the April sunshine. He caught her hand and squeezed it. It was fun to be with Lizzie. He knew that she would want to see everything as he did.

How good it felt to be down among the people and rubbing elbows with them! It was much more fun than sitting up in a window above their heads. Down in the street you could even hear what they said. You could tell how they felt. You could feel the love they all had for the new President.

Lizzie and he had a wonderful time. They walked the length of Broad Way, which didn't take them very long, for one could walk all through New York City in twenty minutes. They stopped when they liked and stared at everything and enjoyed themselves thoroughly. They had been hearing the roar of artillery, and now they heard wild cheers near the wharf.

When they heard the first shrill piping and thumping of the fife-and-drum corps, they made their way to the front row of the people who lined the street on either side.

"Left, right! Left, right!" The men of the fife-and-drum corps marched proudly by. They were dressed in new buff-and-blue uniforms. Their eyes twinkled and the corners of their mouth twisted up as they rolled out the gay marching tune:

> "Yankee Doodle came to town
> Upon a Kentish pony,
> He stuck a feather in his cap
> And called it Macaroni!"

So they had piped and drummed the men who followed them, and, yes, the great general himself, into the battles of the war. Now, with the same fervor they were piping and drumming their chosen President into his place as the leader of the peace years that lay ahead.

"Here they come!" men shouted. "Hurrah for George Washington, the first President of the United States!"

While the men cheered wildly, the women in the windows waved their white handkerchiefs excitedly. They tried to cheer too, but they sounded like chirping sparrows.

Lizzie and Washington cheered as loudly as they could. Washington waved the small silk flag his brother William had bought him. It was a thrilling moment to young Washington Irving.

The President, walking beside Mr. Clinton, the Governor of New York State, came abreast of the lad and his nurse. The men's faces were grave, for they well knew the many duties that lay before George Washington. They kept their eyes straight ahead and walked slowly.

"If he'd only look your way!" Lizzie sighed. "How pleased he would be to know that here was a boy named for him!"

Then suddenly young Washington Irving saw that the President's hands were empty. Who had a better right to carry the flag he had designed? So, not stopping to think, the boy rushed out into the middle of the street.

"Please, sir," he cried, thrusting his tiny silk flag into the President's hand, "here's a flag for you! I only wish it were a bigger one!"

Someone snatched the child back into the crowd. He looked around, startled, for he had lost Lizzie. People milled around him, some smiling at what he had done, one or two disapproving.

"Lizzie! Lizzie!" he called in his piping little voice. "I'm lost, Lizzie! Come and find me!"

People were too intent on watching the rest of the parade to pay any attention to a frightened little boy. He pushed his way through a forest of legs. He had lost his sense of direction. He wasn't sure whether he was going toward or away from Lizzie. He was too short to be able to see which way the parade was going. He had been pushed far back against the houses. Rows of people, ten deep, separated him from the center of the street where the parade was passing.

Then suddenly he was swung up to a broad shoulder and found that he could see again over the heads of most of the people.

"What a way to treat a hero," a man's deep voice said reassuringly, "pushing you around like this and getting you lost! I saw the whole thing. You're a brave lad and I'll find your nurse for you! Keep a sharp lookout for her, like a good lad. She can't be far away."

Washington felt happy and secure now. The man who was carrying him was a neighbor of the Irvings, and Washington had known him ever since he was born. It wasn't long before they saw Lizzie, who rushed forward to claim him. Her blue eyes were shining with pride.

"He's as brave as any Scotch Highlander!" she said, looking proudly at the small boy. From Lizzie there could be no higher praise.

The President's Blessing

"Lizzie will take you to Mr. Hood's to be measured for a new pair of shoes," Mrs. Irving said. She shook her pretty head as she examined the stubbed toes of her youngest child's boots. How he did wear out shoes!

Washington was delighted. He liked to go to the old cobbler's shop. It was down in the basement of a house on Broad Way and it smelled of good things—leather and beeswax and tallow. It also smelled of the tobacco the old man smoked in a short clay pipe. The cobbler worked by candlelight most of the time, as the sun could reach his shop only for an hour or two each day.

The floor around the cobbler's bench was always strewn with bits of leather. Sometimes Mr. Hood would scoop up a handful of these odds and ends and give them to the children who were his customers. At times the leather would be stiff and hard, but often there would be a beautiful soft piece of the most expensive morocco leather from which ladies' shoes were made. And often there would be brilliant pieces of satin, for Mr. Hood made dainty dancing slippers, too. Washington always took these bright bits home to his sister Sarah to be made into dolls' clothes. But the nicer pieces of leather he kept for himself. He liked to look at them and dream of the time when he could see the distant countries from which they came.

Today Lizzie and Washington found Mr. Hood engrossed in turning the sole of a beautiful new pair of boots. They did not know that he was making them for the President.

He did not raise his eyes from his work to see who was standing before him. Lizzie had to call his name twice before he looked up.

The old cobbler pushed his square, silver-rimmed spectacles up on his forehead. Then he smiled at the boy, who was a favorite of his. He had been making Washington Irving's shoes for several years.

"It's not often I have the honor of making boots for two Washingtons at the same time," Mr. Hood said with a twinkle. He put down the large shining boot and took out his measure.

"Foot's growing," he said, "but you'll never be a big man, son. I've been making shoes for a long time and I can tell from the size of a foot at certain stages just how much a boy will grow."

Lizzie scoffed at him. "Washington will grow as big as the next if he eats his good oatmeal," she said. "He just needs to eat more."

But the old cobbler shook his head.

After Washington's feet had been measured and the shoes promised in a week, Mr. Hood hunted carefully through the pile of leather beside his workbench. He selected a piece of red morocco and a piece of shining black leather.

"These are special," he said, thrusting them into Washington's small hand. "They are bits of the leather from which I made the shoes that Mistress Martha Washington and the President himself wore at their Inauguration Ball."

Washington thanked him cordially and put them into his pocket.

When he and Lizzie climbed to street level again the air smelled of flowers and the sea. The sky was such a pure blue that Washington, tipping back his head and staring up at it, said, "It's like my porridge bowl upside down."

They walked hand in hand along Broad Way, enjoying the crisp sweet air, the sunshine and the shop windows.

"America is a generous country," Lizzie told her small charge. "She opens her arms and her heart to all who need her help. Look, yonder is the shop of Grant Thorburn. He lived near by me in Scotland and crossed the great ocean on the very same ship. He was a poor lad then with only a sixpence in his pocket. Now he's a florist and makes bouquets for all the young ladies to carry to the Assemblies that are held in the hotel on Broad Way at Cedar Street. I'll take you some Sunday to his greenhouses in Brooklyn. He's about to move his shop to Liberty Street. These quarters are too small."

"I like the Frenchmen's glove shops best," Washington began. But Lizzie caught his hand so tight that he said, "Ouch."

"Look!" she cried. "There's the great man himself! There's President Washington across the street!" She pointed excitedly toward a shop that the President was just entering.

It was easy to recognize that tall, upright figure, with the white powdered wig, the black
three-cornered hat, the long, blue, military cape
that swung from his shoulders.

Lizzie, still clutching young Washington by
the hand, darted across Broad Way right under
the horses' noses. She ran up the steps of the
shop and opened the door. She pushed the boy
before her into the shop.

"Oh, please, Your Honor," she said breathlessly, "here's a boy who was named for you!"

Mr. Trent, the shopkeeper, wrung his hands.
He was afraid the President would be angry and
take his trade somewhere else. But President
George Washington was a big man in all ways.

His dark eyes, which could be so piercing that
soldiers trembled beneath their cold stare, softened as they came to rest on his young namesake. "So your name is Washington, too," he
said. "Tell me your full name."

The boy spoke up loud and clear as he had been taught. "Washington Irving, sir."

Then the President, looking closer, recognized him. "You're the boy who gave me the flag!" he exclaimed. "The day I marched up Broad Way."

Lizzie sprang forward, afraid her favorite was about to be scolded.

"He meant no harm, Your Honor. He only thought that none was so worthy as you to carry the flag you helped design, sir."

The President smiled and put his hand on Washington Irving's blond head. "I understand," he said. "Tell me, child, what do you plan to do when you grow up?"

The boy tilted back his head and met the black eyes frankly. "I'm going to write books. I'm going to be a sailor first and sail around the world. Then I'll write about what I've seen. Someday I'd like to write a book about you, sir, and tell how brave, kind and just you are."

The President shook his head and smiled. He looked very pleased, but grave, too. "See that you tell the truth!" he said. "I've made my mistakes, too, you know. A book about a person is not good unless it tells the truth."

"I'll remember, sir," Washington promised.

"Now, here's my blessing, lad. May life bring you what you want and may your dreams come true!" President Washington laid his hand on his namesake's head and blessed him.

Somehow Lizzie managed to get herself and Washington Irving out of the shop. They hurried home, hand in hand, through the gathering purple twilight. In their hearts was a deep and lasting devotion to the great man who was their President.

A New School

"How MUCH is four and eight?" Mr. Irving asked his youngest son one morning.

Washington put his hands behind his back and counted slowly on his fingers. "Twelve," he said at last.

His father frowned. He wasn't a bit pleased. "You counted on your fingers!" he accused.

Washington hung his head and nodded.

"But surely you are old enough to be able to do a simple sum like that in your head," his father said. "You have been at Mrs. Kilmaster's school for two years. You read very well, but what about your arithmetic?"

"I don't like arithmetic, Father," Washington answered. "I can read because I like to. I want to read every book in the world. But I don't want to do every sum of arithmetic in the world."

"Everyone must know arithmetic," Mr. Irving explained. "How do you suppose I could be a merchant if I didn't know how to add and subtract and multiply? It's fine to read books, but you must learn to do some things you don't like, as well as what you like." He shook his head. "I suspect the time has come when you must go to school with your older brothers."

Washington thought for a dreadful moment that he was going to cry. He didn't want to leave Mrs. Kilmaster. He loved the large sunny schoolroom with its flowers and gay books. He liked Mike the parrot, who had learned to say, "Scat, scat, you bad black cat!" He liked the deep old garden in the rear of the school where he had spent so many happy recess hours.

But a boy of six and a half is too old to cry. So he slipped through the garden gate and went to the public well at the corner of William Street and got himself a big drink of icy cold water. That made him feel better.

Mr. Irving took him to the new school the next morning. This adventure was very different from his first day at kind Mrs. Kilmaster's. He walked sedately beside his father. Mr. Irving marched along in his good black cloth suit and his three-cornered black beaver hat. His silver-headed cane and the silver buckles on his black shoes twinkled in the sunlight. Washington did not run ahead or skip this morning!

Mr. Irving suddenly sensed what was going on in his son's mind. He looked down at him and smiled.

"Come, come!" he said pleasantly. "There's no need to look so woeful. School isn't a place where they chop off your head."

"John and Peter have told me that Mr. Romaine whips the boys when they are bad," Washington answered stoutly.

"Then you must see that you are never bad," his father pointed out. But the sight of the white face beside him was too much. He loved his youngest son dearly and he wanted to see him smile. "I'll tell you what we'll do," he went on, slowing his pace so they could talk more comfortably. "If you're good for a whole week and don't get any whippings, I'll take you to the circus to see the elephant. It has come all the way from India in a sailing vessel. And there's a lion, too, you know. The owners take him outside of the city every night so he won't disturb our sleep by his violent roaring. You'll like the circus, won't you?"

Washington didn't have to say anything. His sparkling eyes told his father all he wanted to know. The boy was happy again.

Mr. Benjamin Romaine's school was on Fulton Street. It was a tall narrow brick house, one of a row, and there was no garden in front. The door was painted a drab olive green and, instead of a bright and shining brass knocker, there was an ugly black iron one.

Mr. Romaine opened the door. He was tall and dark, and Washington actually had to bend backward to look up into his stern face. Washington's knees began to tremble. He knew that Mr. Romaine had been a captain in the Army in the Revolutionary War and that he was very strict. Even the Indian elephant and the roaring lion failed to comfort him now.

"I want you to put some arithmetic into my son's head," Mr. Irving told him. "He can't tell me what four and eight add up to without counting on his fingers."

Mr. Romaine shook his head. "We'll see what we can do to remedy that!" he said gravely.

Poor Washington! Mr. Romaine was a much better teacher than Mrs. Kilmaster. He kept pounding arithmetic into the lad's head until he began to understand it a little. But he was most unhappy. He didn't give a copper penny if six and six made twelve or thirteen or eleven. But Mr. Romaine cared and he soon made his pupil begin to care, too.

Washington managed to escape Mr. Romaine's birch rod for a whole week. His father took him to the circus where the elephant from India did marvelous tricks and let the braver children ride on his back. Washington rode several times. He kept his eyes shut so he wouldn't see the sawdust ring around which the elephant walked majestically. He pretended he was riding through the jungles of India, and the roars of the lion in his cage made it seem very real indeed. He would visit India when he took that trip around the world.

Except for the arithmetic lessons, Washington enjoyed the new school. The library was very good, and he was allowed to choose and read any book he wished. Although he liked to read so much, he liked writing better and turned out composition after composition that brought him very high marks indeed.

Arithmetic examples seemed to Washington like a series of hurdles over which he must leap every day. He was sure that someday he would find one he couldn't get over. And he did!

He had been wrestling with it for half an hour and his nose was prickly from unshed tears, when his best friend, Tom Farley, came to find him.

"How about a game of catch?" Tom asked, throwing a ball as high as the low ceiling of the room would permit, then catching it expertly.

"I can't, until I've finished this sum," Washington explained. "I've tried several ways, but I can't seem to get it right."

Tom sat down beside him and in a few minutes had worked it out neatly.

"I don't know how you do it so quickly!" Washington sighed admiringly.

"It's nothing. I happen to understand and enjoy arithmetic," Tom explained modestly.

"Enjoy arithmetic!" Washington cried. "I hate it. How could anybody like arithmetic?"

"You like to read and to write compositions," Tom said. "I don't. I never can think of anything to write about."

Washington stared at his friend. "But that's fun," he said.

Tom laughed good-naturedly. "Not to me. I hate to write compositions as much as you hate to do sums."

Washington's face suddenly lighted up. "I know what we'll do!" he cried excitedly. "I've got a good idea. Why don't you do my sums for me and I'll write all your compositions?"

"That would be dandy," Tom agreed enthusiastically. He, too, thought it an excellent idea.

So for a while Washington Irving wrote all of Tom Farley's compositions for him. Tom leaped from the bottom of the English class to the top next to Washington. And Washington did the same thing in the arithmetic class.

Mr. Romaine knew that something was wrong. He liked both boys and he knew they were bright, but they were not that bright. So he watched and waited and finally discovered what was going on.

"Washington Irving and Tom Farley will please stay in this room at recess," he said one morning. The two boys exchanged glances. They knew they had been found out.

Mr. Romaine looked very stern seated behind his desk. The two boys, their hands clasped behind them as they had been taught to do, stood before him, feeling small and dejected.

Mr. Romaine brought his black brows together and his dark eyes seemed to look right through them.

"Washington Irving, you have been writing Tom Farley's compositions, and he has been doing your sums," Mr. Romaine said severely.

Washington lifted his blond head and met his teacher's eyes squarely.

"Yes, sir," he answered truthfully, although his voice trembled and his knees were shaking.

"Didn't you know that was a deceitful thing?" Mr. Romaine asked.

Washington shook his head. "It just seemed so much easier and simpler that way, sir. Sums are too much for me, but I like to write compositions. Tom hates them, but he likes to do sums. We thought we'd help each other out."

"But can't you see that neither of you was learning anything?" Mr. Romaine pointed out. "You were cheating yourselves as well as me."

74

Both boys looked flabbergasted. They hadn't realized the seriousness of what they had done. As Washington had said, it had seemed so much simpler and easier the way they'd worked it out.

"You must be punished," Mr. Romaine said sternly. He reached for the birch switch he always kept beside his desk. "You shall be whipped. Ten lashes for each of you!"

Washington grew white. He dreaded being switched more than anything else in the world. He had never been whipped in his life and it would be humiliation before the school. But he pushed Tom Farley to one side and said bravely, "I'm to blame, sir! I suggested the whole thing. Tom only agreed to my idea. Please don't whip him, sir. I'll take twenty lashes."

Mr. Romaine looked at his youngest pupil and his dark eyes softened. He was proud of the boy but he would not let him off. He believed in stern punishment.

"Please step up to the desk, Washington," he said. "Tom Farley, go back to your seat."

Tom Farley hid his face while Washington was being switched. He couldn't bear to look at his friend's white, set face.

"One, two, three, four . . ." Mr. Romaine began to count as he raised the switch and brought it down on the slender little shoulders.

It was over at last and Washington went back to his place beside Tom Farley. "It didn't hurt too much," he whispered. He put out his hand to comfort his friend, who seemed to have suffered more than he had.

Mr. Romaine kept Washington after school. "There is something I want to talk to you about," he said.

When all the children had left he walked to where Washington Irving still sat at his desk. He put a friendly, strong hand on the boy's shoulder.

"I wanted you to stay so I could tell you how proud I am of you," he said. "You could have shared your punishment with Tom Farley and had only ten strokes from the birch rod, instead of twenty. But you felt the blame was yours and you took your punishment like a gentleman and a soldier. You are worthy to bear the name of the greatest gentleman and soldier I know, George Washington!"

And after that Mr. Romaine always referred to his youngest pupil as "the little general."

A White Christmas

Washington sat at the desk in his sister Sarah's room. He was writing verses for her to tuck into the toe of the pair of slippers she had made for a Christmas present for their father. Sarah was very particular.

His face was screwed up and the red tip of his tongue showed at the corner of his mouth. His family said he always made faces when he wrote, and sometimes they teased him.

"There!" he said, putting down the quill pen and sprinkling sand over the paper before him to dry the ink. "That's a good poem. Listen! How do you like this?"

"When winter winds blow
And redden your nose,
May these pretty slippers
Keep warming your toes!"

"I don't like it," Sarah declared. "It makes me
sound too conceited. Maybe Father won't think
they're pretty. Father, not I, should be the one
to say they're pretty."

Washington thought that over. "I'll try
again," he said.

At last he put down the pen and read:

"When winter winds
Make red your nose,
May these new slippers
Warm your toes!"

Sarah smiled. "That's much better!" she said.

Washington was proud of his versemaking.
There was a poem for each member of his family, but best of all he liked the one he'd written
for his mother.

"When all the Christmas fun is through,
   And all the sugarplums are eaten,
How glad I am to have you here
   A ma who can't be beaten!"

"I don't think it's as pretty as some you've written," Sarah said when he read it aloud to her.
"But you certainly got into it the way we all feel
about Mother."

A loud knock on the front door sent the children running to open it. Their sister Ann, her
husband, Richard Dodge, and their tall brother
William stood on the tiny porch. They had come
down from the frozen banks of the Mohawk
River to spend Christmas with the Irvings.

The children shrieked with joy and threw
themselves on the muffled figures, drawing them
into the warm parlor.

"Mother! Mother!" Washington shouted.
"William and Ann and Richard have come home
for Christmas!"

Mrs. Irving flew in from the kitchen where she had been helping Lizzie with the evening meal and embraced them.

"This is the nicest Christmas present I can have," she declared, "all my children together under the same roof."

After supper was over the family gathered in the parlor. Washington sat spellbound with the others, listening to the stories of the northland.

Wild animals and Indians still roamed then through the Adirondack Mountains.

"I'd like to see it all for myself," Washington declared. "I'd like to wander through the woods and see Indians and wild animals."

"You shall come and stay with us when you are older," his sister Ann said, bending to kiss his eager face. He promised he would.

At last Mr. Irving and Peter and John arrived with the Christmas tree. It was a huge one, twelve feet high.

"We had to go almost as far as Greenwich Village to get it," Mr. Irving said, blowing on his cold fingers and holding them toward the leaping flames. The tree was a beauty, tall and full and just right for the space between the windows in the family living room.

For weeks the younger members of the Irving family had been gilding nuts, stringing popcorn and making paper chains with which to decorate the tree. This year Mr. Irving had a surprise for them. He took a box of tiny wax tapers out of his coat pocket and some wire holders with which to fasten them to the tree.

"These came from Germany," he explained. "The tree will be beautiful this year."

Later that evening the whole family helped to trim the tree. Mrs. Irving's people had been English, and she had brought many of the old and well-loved customs with her from the mother country. The Irvings made a great fuss over

Christmas and looked forward to celebrating the holiday for months beforehand.

The tree was as lovely as Mr. Irving had thought it would be. All the presents were stacked beneath it. These were not to be opened until the next morning. The candles were blown out and would be relighted the next day.

"Bedtime now," Mrs. Irving said to Sarah and Washington. The other Irving children were old enough to stay up for an hour or two longer and sing carols to the soft accompaniment of Ann's playing on the spinet.

But Washington couldn't get to sleep. He lay in the trundle bed under the warm hand-knit blankets and tossed from side to side. He thought about the tree in the parlor below and how bare and lonely the place in the woods must be since his father had cut it down. He wondered if the tree was happy and liked being decked out in ornaments and strung with popcorn and lighted from top to bottom with the tiny tapers from Germany. Perhaps it would like its regular winter coat of snow better.

He thought of the presents he'd find under the tree in the morning. He hoped his father had bought him the set of books he'd asked for. And then he thought about the shopwindows and how gay they'd been decked out in toys and sugarplums and cakes. The cakes had been made in the shape of boys and girls and of little houses, with white icing for snow on their brown roofs.

He heard the soft lisping sound of real snow against the windowpane. What a pleasant sound it was when one was snug in bed! How wonderful to have snow! Tomorrow would be a white Christmas. He pulled the blankets higher around his shoulders and snuggled deeper into the feather mattress. Soon he was asleep.

He awoke to a world as beautiful as a fairy tale. He knew he would never forget it.

"Merry Christmas!" he shouted, hopping out of bed. The whole house rang with the happy cry as the other members of the family dressed and ran downstairs.

Washington's eyes sparkled with delight as he got his first view of the family living room. He could feel the warmth of Christmas everywhere.

Such wonderful gifts there were for everyone! Washington received not only a set of *The World Displayed*, accounts of voyages and travels selected from the writers of all nations, but also *Robinson Crusoe* and *The Arabian Nights*.

He crept in behind the tree where, hidden by its branches, he could enjoy his treasures.

There Lizzie found him and called him to breakfast. Washington spooned up his porridge as quickly as possible. He wanted to get back to his gifts. He sometimes liked the world of imagination he found in books better than he liked the real world.

Lizzie came in carrying a plate of her famous biscuits. She was usually smiling, but today she had tears in her big blue eyes.

"What is it, Lizzie?" Mrs. Irving inquired kindly. "Have you burned yourself?"

"Oh, no, ma'am! It's not that. The poor Downey children were at the back door asking for a bit of bread for their Christmas dinner. I gave them some, ma'am, and a few cakes, too, knowing you wouldn't mind."

"Of course not, Lizzie! You did just right. I only hope you gave them enough." Mrs. Irving's soft heart was generous, too. "I'll stop by their place after church and take them one of our roasted chickens and some milk for the baby."

Nobody noticed that Washington had put down his spoon and was listening to every word. Nobody paid much attention when he begged to be excused and slipped away. He went back to the tree and looked down at all his gifts.

There were so many for him! Nobody had forgotten him. He dropped down to his knees and went over every one of them. There were plenty of toys as well as the books. There were bags of sugarplums and boxes of cakes, too.

He smoothed out a great white woolen muffler his sister Catherine had knitted for him. He put all the candy and the cakes and the toys in the center and tied up the four corners. He carried the bundle up to his room and got his cap and coat. Then he slipped quietly down the back stairs, through the hall and let himself out the front door without being seen. He crossed the garden and opened the gate into snowy William Street. He was no longer thinking about what a beautiful Christmas day this was.

He walked swiftly because he was afraid if someone saw him he might be called back. He had a long way to go to reach the poor street on the outskirts of town where the Downey family

lived, but he found the house at last and put his
bundle on the doorstep. Then he rapped three
times on the door as loudly as he could and called,
"Merry Christmas!"

When he heard footsteps coming he turned and ran away. He hid around the corner until he thought they had had time to open the door and take in the bundle. Then he poked his head around to see if the doorstep was empty. It was!

He ran home and joined the others, now all busy opening their gifts and exclaiming over them. Washington sat down with a book.

Sarah came and sat down beside him on the floor. She had filled the skirt of her long red dress with presents and she dumped them down between them.

"I'm going to show you everything I got. Then you must show me your gifts," she said. "Did you like the drum I gave you? You always said you wanted one."

Washington had to tell her what he had done with all his presents, except his books.

Some of his brothers and sisters were provoked that he had given away their gifts.

But his mother understood.

When she went up to kiss him good night she asked if he had had a happy day.

"It was the nicest Christmas I ever had," he told her. "I like to help other people."

"Your father asked me to give you this last gift from him," Mrs. Irving said. She held out a note folded into the shape of a cocked hat.

It was a letter to Mr. Downey telling him if he would apply at Mr. Irving's warehouse he would find a job waiting for him!

"You may take the note to Mr. Downey tomorrow morning," Mrs. Irving said.

"This is the nicest present of all," Washington Irving declared.

A New Friend

WASHINGTON IRVING and Tom Farley trudged along William Street with fishing poles over their shoulders. They were on their way to Fresh Water Pond, or Collect Pond, as it was called by some, for an afternoon of fishing.

This lovely fresh water pond was a mile or so from Washington's home, but the boys enjoyed every minute of the walk. There was always something to see, something to talk about. Many people lived in the part of William Street where the Irvings' house stood. But as the street went northward and passed the city limits, there were fewer and fewer houses.

91

The neat paving gave way to a dusty country road. Blackberry bushes grew on both sides of it. Timid little wild animals lurked in a tangle of underbrush.

Some people thought this district would be built upon someday and the city might even reach to Fourteenth Street. But there were others, including Washington and Tom, who thought that this was a very silly idea and hoped it would never happen. What would become of their fishing if the City Fathers had a canal dug and drained off the water of Collect Pond as they threatened to do? Didn't it take a good twenty minutes to walk from one end of the city to the other? That was large enough for any city!

William Street ended at Pearl Street. Here the boys cut across and turned into Magazine Street, scarcely more than a narrow, winding footpath. They drew closer to each other as they neared an old weather-beaten house.

People said this house was haunted by the ghost of an old miser. He had loved his gold even better than himself, and for lack of food had starved to death. The shutters of the house had a peculiar way of flapping, even when there wasn't any wind. The front door had been known to open by itself on its creaky hinges.

"I don't believe in ghosts," Tom Farley said stoutly as they drew nearer.

"I'm not sure whether I do or not," Washington answered. He liked to pretend he half-believed in them because he enjoyed the fright tickling his spine.

Although it was broad daylight he stole a look over his shoulder and lowered his voice as if he expected someone might overhear him. "Once I thought I saw a white figure at one of the upstairs windows," he added in a low whisper.

"You've got too much imagination, Washington," Tom Farley said uneasily.

They were abreast now of the old house with its paneless windows, broken shutters and creaking door. Tom began to whistle a trifle off key. A large black cloud darkened the sun. The wind blew through the leafless branches of a tall sycamore tree, making an eerie sound as the dry twigs rubbed together.

Then something big and gray flew out of one of the upstairs windows. It made a queer screeching sound and disappeared in the woods that surrounded the old house. Washington and Tom took to their heels. They didn't stop until they had reached the pleasant shore of Collect Pond.

"I suppose you're going to say we saw a ghost," Tom Farley said a trifle breathlessly as he squatted down to put a big fat worm on his hook.

"Well, what did you think it was?" Washington demanded, making a move to bait his hook.

"It was just an old owl!" Tom said firmly, tossing his line into the water.

Soon something tugged at it. He pulled in a good-sized perch.

"Fishing is going to be good," he said. Both boys forgot everything but the joy in the sport.

The shores of Collect Pond sloped gently and were thickly wooded. The fresh water bubbled up from deep, hidden springs. It was cold and sweet to drink. There was a lazy charm about the neighborhood that delighted all young fishermen and made it a favorite place for them to spend a free afternoon.

Washington walked slowly along the bank. So far Tom had had all the luck and Washington hoped to change his in another pool. But what he found instead sent him running as fast as he could back to his friend.

"There's an old rowboat pulled up on the shore. Come and see! Now we can row to the island in the middle of the pond. We've always wanted to."

Washington was so excited he began to stutter. "And we can h-hunt for the treasures that are s-supposed to be b-buried there!"

"Not me!" Tom Farley said stoutly. "Money you find that way isn't lucky. My father says so. Look at all the things that have happened to people who hunted for Captain Kidd's treasure. I don't want to find treasure that will bring me only bad luck."

"Well, we won't look for money then. But I want to see the island. It's haunted. Over a hundred years ago an Indian killed a fur trader on that island."

"So I suppose you think we'll see his ghost," Tom said, trying to sound scornful. Washington knew many stories of old New York and they all interested Tom. But there were times when he didn't want to encourage his friend too much, and this was one of them. "Anyway, I told you I didn't believe in ghosts," he added.

"Then let's hurry," Washington said. He climbed into the boat and Tom followed.

The island in the center of Collect Pond was called Magazine Island because a great deal of ammunition had been kept there in a storeroom or "magazine" during the Revolutionary War.

The sky was black with clouds now, and the wind grew stronger and the waves wore little whitecaps. A few drops of rain spattered against the boys' faces, but they didn't turn back. This was too good an adventure. They certainly were not afraid of a few drops of rain, and they might not have the use of a boat again.

Tom rowed the boat to shore and the boys hopped out. The island was not densely wooded. Lightning had struck in several places, leaving a few tall bare trunks of splintered pine trees. The rest of the growth was low and there were many thick bushes. The wind was strong and the bare branches creaked above their heads.

"I-I'm glad I'm n-not afraid of ghosts," Tom said in a quavering voice.

"It's sort of spooky," Washington began, but his voice broke. He had to repeat what he had been saying in a louder voice.

"You don't have to shout!" Tom Farley grumbled. He had lowered his own voice until it sounded queer and shivery.

They walked toward a clump of thick bushes. Then unexpectedly they heard a deep groan. Washington felt a tingling at the nape of his neck and that pleasant thrill of fright down his spine. Tom stood stock-still, and his red cheeks lost some of their bright color.

"What was that?" he whispered. Then they heard the rustle of dead leaves, the snapping of dry twigs. Not waiting to hear anything else, they turned and fled back to the boat and threw themselves into it. Each took an oar and rowed as fast as he could away from the island.

When they had put fifteen or twenty feet between them and whatever or whoever had been hiding in the bushes, they stopped and dared to raise their heads and look back.

"Look!" Washington cried, pointing. "It was only a dog. And he's been hurt."

The poor beast stood on the shore and gazed at them with sad brown eyes. His ribs showed through his tan hide. Burs were matted in his thick tail and he was a sorry sight indeed.

"Somebody has taken him there and left him to die!" Washington cried. "I'm going back and take him home."

They rowed back to the island.

The grateful but weak dog had to be lifted into the boat. He lay across Washington's knees and licked his hand feebly from time to time.

"Mother will know what to do for him," Washington said when they got to shore. "Come and help me, Tom."

They took turns carrying the dog home. His left hind leg was broken.

Mrs. Irving did know just what to do. Most mothers had to know what to do in an emergency. Doctors were few and far apart and sometimes it was impossible to get one for days.

"Bring some hot water, Washington, and some bandages from the linen chest and two pieces of smooth wood for a splint," she told her son.

Later, when the dog's broken leg had been set and bound tight and he was resting on a soft cushion before the fire, Mrs. Irving said, "What are you going to name your new friend?"

Washington looked at the dog for a while. Then he said, "I think I'll call him Black Spot. He has a funny black ring around his left eye."

"Very well," Mrs. Irving agreed. "And now he must be introduced to Gussie. She has been our only pet for a long time and she may be jealous of a dog around here."

Washington found Gussie asleep by the kitchen fire. She was rolled up into a tight black ball. But he woke her up and carried her into the parlor and put her down beside Black Spot. Gussie reared back on her haunches and spat at him. Black Spot wagged his tail feebly to show he wanted to be friends. Gussie spat again and the poor tired dog closed his eyes and tried to pay no attention. Then Gussie did an amazing thing. She went closer and sniffed the dog all over, making little growly noises in her throat.

Washington looked at his mother and smiled. "I think she's ashamed of the way she has acted," he said. "I think she's decided to make friends."

And she had. Gussie and Black Spot were good friends from that time on.

Oh, for the Life of a Sailor

BLACK SPOT bounded after the stick Washington threw for him. Black Spot's leg had healed. He had fattened out and become a very handsome and satisfactory dog.

He brought the stick back and laid it at his young master's feet. Washington bent to pick it up and throw it again when a voice that somehow seemed familiar attracted his attention.

"Hello!" it said.

Washington turned and ran to the gate. A tall blond young man stood outside. He was smiling and his face was friendly and kind and somehow familiar.

102

"Forgotten me?" he asked. "I'm Peter Gaans-voot. I'm just back from a trip around the world. I've seen wonderful things."

Washington sprang forward with a glad shout. Five years had passed since Peter had shown him New York Bay with its pretty green islands and ships with white sails, but he had never forgotten. He had often talked of his friend.

The tall tanned youth seemed like a person come to life out of a book. Washington had thought of him often and wondered what adventures he was having in the distant countries Washington so longed to see.

"Come in!" he cried and swung wide the gate. Black Spot rushed forward and barked his approval of this old friend.

Peter Gaansvoot carried a sea chest on his right shoulder. It was covered with leather and studded with nails. He swung it easily to his left shoulder so he could shake hands with the boy.

"It's been a long time," Peter said, smiling down at his young friend. "You've grown."

"I'm ten," Washington said proudly. "And I still want to be a sailor."

Peter laughed. "It's a hard life," he said.

Mr. and Mrs. Irving were delighted to see Peter again. They had liked the slim Dutch lad who had been so kind to their young son five years before. They liked the straight-backed, broad-shouldered young man he had grown into. Peter's blue eyes were still frank. His yellow hair, bleached almost white by tropic sun, still had a boyish cowlick.

"You must stay to supper," Mrs. Irving said hospitably.

Peter accepted gladly and put his sea chest behind the door out of everyone's way.

After supper he asked to be excused. He went and got the chest and carried it into the living room. He put it down before the cheerful fire.

In it was a gift for everyone. There were a lovely lace and ivory fan for Mrs. Irving and a small globe for Washingtor.

Washington thought there had never been a nicer gift. He pored over it all evening. His finger traced out the voyages he planned to take someday. Even the younger members of the family sat up late, listening to the stories Peter told of his adventures. Washington was more determined than ever to become a sailor.

He started that very night to put himself and Black Spot into training.

"No more feather beds for us," he said sternly. "Peter says sailors sleep on hard wooden bunks. We'll sleep on the floor tonight."

He had his room to himself now. Ebenezer and John had moved into the rooms William and Ann had left vacant when they went north to live. Washington had graduated from the little trundle bed to the great four-poster.

He took a blanket from it and spread it on the floor. Then he covered himself with another. Black Spot curled up in an unhappy ball beside him. They were very uncomfortable. A draft blew through a crack under the door. The floor was very hard. Neither of them slept well that night, but they would not give up.

The next day Washington begged Lizzie for a piece of salt pork. Peter had said salt pork was what sailors mostly had to eat. He and Black Spot divided it, but they hated it.

Night after night, day after day, Washington kept himself and Black Spot on their strict training. Washington grew so stiff from sleeping on the floor that he could scarcely get up and dress for school in the mornings. He lost weight and his mother worried about him.

On the sixth day he woke up to find that Black Spot had forsaken him! The dog was stretched out comfortably on the soft feather bed!

Washington's stomach felt upset and he had a sore throat and the sniffles. His mother put her cool hand on his head, when he went down to breakfast, and sent him back to his room.

"Go to bed," she said. "I'll be right up with a dose of medicine for you."

How good it was to climb into his comfortable bed! How soft the feather mattress felt beneath his aching back and limbs! How eagerly he ate the good breakfast his mother brought him after he had taken the medicine she had prepared! He didn't think he could have eaten even one more piece of salt pork.

Black Spot came to see him later. He gave a deep sigh of content as he jumped up on the bed and stretched himself out in his usual place at Washington's feet.

The boy and the dog slept for sixteen hours. They were tired out from their nights on the hard drafty floor and their diet of salt pork.

Peter Gaansvoot was sitting beside the bed when Washington opened his eyes. He put out a strong brown hand and patted the lad's shoulder. "Feeling better?" he asked.

Washington nodded. "I wanted to be a sailor and take Black Spot along to be a mascot."

Peter shook his blond head and smiled. "A sailor's life is a hard life, lad, as I told you. And it's not for the likes of you and Black Spot. You'll go around the world someday. Never fear! But you'll be traveling with a set of notebooks and a handful of pens, writing down all that you see and hear and do. You're going to be an author. Had you forgotten?"

Washington lay on his back and stared at the ceiling for a long, long time. He was thinking. Finally he said, "Maybe you're right, Peter. Maybe Black Spot and I wouldn't make very good sailors. We tried to be sailors on the land, and look at us!"

Peter laughed and patted his shoulder again.

"Someday you and I will travel on the same ship together. Wait and see!"

Washington felt comforted. He'd see the world someday, but as a passenger, just as Peter said he should. It would be more pleasant to travel comfortably and write books about the different places he visited.

A Plate of Honey Cake

WASHINGTON entered the schoolroom breathlessly. He had slept late on this first day of school and had had to run all the way. He slipped quietly into his seat, hoping Mr. Romaine wouldn't be too harsh this first day.

When he got his breath he looked about to see whether there were any new pupils. There was just one! She sat in the seat ahead of Washington and the sunlight fell through the window on her hair. It looked so alive that Washington thought it might feel warm like a fire if you held your hands out to it. He had never seen hair like it.

He was sure that a girl who had such beautiful hair must be the prettiest girl in the world. He lingered behind the others when the class was dismissed at recess and laid a bag of sugarplums on her desk. She thanked him that afternoon with a sweet smile.

The next day he brought her a scarlet quill pen, the point sharpened to perfection. The third day he confessed to Tom Farley that he thought Ann Trent was beautiful and he liked her.

"What!" Tom shouted. "That bean pole with the carroty hair! You're crazy, Washington."

But Washington thought Tom was crazy not to see how pretty Ann was, and what did it matter if she was a head taller than he? He admired her height and her slenderness.

When he heard Ann was going to have a leading part in a school play he made up his mind to be in it, too. So he went to Mr. Romaine and asked if he might play a certain character.

112

"It's a long and difficult part," Mr. Romaine said in surprise, for Washington had never wanted to act before. "And I had thought of giving it to an older boy."

"Please let me try," Washington begged, so Mr. Romaine said he could.

Washington's sister Catherine helped him learn the part, which was indeed difficult. He worked hard for the next two weeks. By then he had the part learned perfectly.

The great day came at last and the Irving family arrived at the school very early so they would be sure of getting good seats. They found fine ones in the second row.

The young actors and actresses were in a room off the stage, waiting for the curtain to rise. They were excited and restless.

Washington thought Ann looked pretty in her long white flowing robe and with a kerchief over part of her flaming hair.

For his part he had to have his hands and face covered with lampblack and wear a black stocking tightly knotted over his blond hair. When he looked at himself in the glass he was almost sorry he had asked Mr. Romaine if he could be in the play. His grayish blue eyes looked startling, rimmed around by the lampblack. Ann might not like him dressed like this!

Refreshments were being served after the play. They were spread out on a long table in the back of the room. One of the older boys smuggled a plate of honey cake to the cast.

"Have some," he said, passing it around.

Washington helped himself to a big piece. He was very fond of honey cake, and he was sure he would have time to finish it before the play started. Besides, it would help him to forget his blacked-up face and hands and comical cap.

He stuffed the sticky mass into his mouth and began to munch it. How delicious it tasted!

Suddenly the sound of music came to his ears. He was horrified, for it was his cue to step out on the stage and into his part.

His jaws moved up and down, up and down. His face grew red from the effort to swallow the honey cake. But the sticky stuff refused to grow smaller and clung to the roof of his mouth.

Mr. Romaine opened the door and beckoned. His dark face was stern. The music that came first had been played over three times. The actors and actresses who were already on the stage were waiting. So was the audience!

Poor Washington stepped out on the stage, his mouth still full of honey cake. He faced the audience, his jaws still working. They thought he was trying to say his lines. They felt sorry for him. They thought he was suffering from stage fright. He could only roll his light eyes that seemed so large in his blackened face and shake his head and go on chewing.

His sister Catherine thought that he was suffering from stage fright and that he had forgotten his lines. She leaned forward and tried to prompt him.

Mr. Romaine, in the wings with the prompter's book, whispered, "Get on with it! You're holding up the whole play!"

Poor, poor Washington! He was in a plight. There was only one thing to do and he did it. He turned his back on the audience, stuck his finger in his mouth, dug out the gooey mass, wrapped it in his handkerchief, thrust his handkerchief into the long sleeve of the robe he wore and turned around to the audience.

"Better to die ten thousand thousand deaths
Than wound my honor . . ."

he began. Then the humor of the whole scene broke over him and he had to fight down a wild desire to laugh. So did the audience.

116

But his voice grew clear and loud as he went on and he soon forgot everything in the part he was playing.

A sigh of relief went up from the audience. Catherine and the family settled back to enjoy themselves. Mr. Romaine mopped his face and went back to following the promptbook. He didn't need it as far as Washington was concerned. The boy knew every word.

A Trip in a Stagecoach

"It is an ill wind that blows nobody good," Mr. Irving said as he helped Washington into his seat in the stagecoach. "If you hadn't had one of your winter colds and if it hadn't hung on longer than usual, you wouldn't be taking this trip to visit your brother William in Tarrytown. You'd have waited until your mother or I could go with you. This is your first trip alone."

He stood aside so that big Tom, the Irvings' Negro servant, might store the small brassbound trunk under Washington's feet. That was the only place one could put luggage on a stagecoach. There was very little room for it.

Washington laughed. He agreed with his father. He thought he was very lucky to be going off alone on a trip to Tarrytown. He had always wanted to travel and Tarrytown on the Hudson was thirty-six miles away! It seemed a thrilling adventure!

William lived there now. He had married and left the wilderness of the Mohawk River.

Washington's father and big Tom said goodby and watched the stagecoach roll out of sight.

At first Washington was too excited to notice that the hard wooden seat had no back, and that his trunk, small though it was, made his short legs stick out uncomfortably. He was wedged in between a fat gentleman and a stout woman. The fat man wore a beaver hat stuffed with papers which he took out and read as they rattled along. The stout woman wore a huge scarlet bonnet with a green feather. She carried a great many bundles and a covered bird cage.

Washington's legs soon went to sleep. He began to twist and turn and try to get them to rest on the floor. To make matters worse, the smelly black leather curtains had been lowered on both sides of the coach to keep out the cold and a faint drizzle that started as they crossed the bridge over the Harlem River. Washington couldn't distract his mind from his numb legs by gazing at the scenery. He would have liked to, since this was his first trip away from home.

The woman with the green feather gave him a poke. "Sit still, boy!" she commanded. "It's uncomfortable enough as it is without you wriggling around!"

Washington tried to be still but his nose began to itch, and then his back, and then he began to itch all over. He tried to scratch the places he could reach, without bothering the persons on each side of him, but it seemed only to make things worse. Even the soles of his feet itched.

"Land o' mercy, what ails you, lad?" the stout lady asked crossly. "Sit still!"

"My legs have gone to sleep and I itch all over," Washington said miserably.

The fat gentleman in the beaver hat laughed and put away his papers. "I know those symptoms well. They come from sitting still too long. Come, stand up before me for a minute or two. I'll balance you."

Washington scrambled awkwardly to his feet. At first his legs seemed to refuse to hold him, and the pain, like pins and needles being stuck into him, was terrible. The kind man in the beaver hat held the back of his coat to steady him. After a while he began to feel much better. He was no longer numb. .

"Thank you very much, sir," he said politely when he sat down again.

"What is your name?" the stout man asked.

"Washington Irving, sir," he answered.

The stout woman turned around and squealed. "Did you go to Mrs. Kilmaster's school on Anne street a few years ago?"

"Yes, ma'am," Washington nodded.

"I've heard my sister-in-law, Mrs. Kilmaster, speak of you. You were always getting into mischief because you had too much imagination. And you didn't like arithmetic."

Washington laughed. "I still don't like arithmetic. I'm going to be a writer when I am older."

"That's what my sister-in-law said you were always telling her. Well, young man, what are you going to write about?"

"You and people like you that I meet when I travel all over the world. I am going to write about what I see. I'm going to write about George Washington, too," he told her.

"Land o' mercy!" she cried in amusement. "What can you write about me? I've never done anything interesting!"

"How nice you turned out to be. I thought at first you were going to be very cross," he answered frankly.

The man in the beaver hat chuckled. "I'll buy that book," he said. Then he added, "I'm on my way into the wilderness. I'm a fur trader and I hope to establish a small settlement on the Columbia River. I'll call it Astoria. There are many Indians around there and the country abounds in wild animals. Someday when you are grown-up, perhaps you'll visit me there. My name is John Jacob Astor."

"If you like I shall write a book about Astoria when I am older," Washington offered.

Mr. Astor chuckled. He hadn't liked anyone in a long time so well as he liked this clear-eyed, outspoken lad.

"If you turn out to be a successful writer, I'll keep you to that promise!" he said. "Volumes could be written about Astoria."

"And do you know who is in that cage?" Mrs. Kilmaster's sister-in-law inquired. She had got over her crossness.

"It can't possibly be Mike!" Washington cried in delight.

"No other!" she said and whisked the cover off the cage with a flourish.

There sat Mike, his green feathers ruffled, a surly look on his face. He didn't like the jolting of the stagecoach any better than the human passengers did.

"Oh, Mike, I'm glad to see you!" Washington exclaimed. "Remember me, Mike? Washington Irving? And do you remember Gussie?"

Mike opened one wicked black eye and saluted smartly as he had been taught to do when he heard the great general's name. Then he said in a loud rasping voice that startled the other occupants of the coach, "Scat, scat, you bad black cat!" He had not forgotten.

Tarrytown

TARRYTOWN was a sleepy old village on the quiet shores of the Hudson River. It had been settled by the Dutch, who are a slow-moving, placid people. Nobody had ever been seen to hurry up and down its steep, hilly streets. Good nature oozed from its inhabitants, and the very animals were good-natured, too. Everything in life moved at a slower pace than it did in the bustling little city of New York at the tip end of Manhatan Island. Tarrytown was a very pleasant place to live in, and everyone who lived there was happy. William Irving loved it, and so did young Washington.

William's house was a cozy place on a side street. Soon there would be flowers in the garden. A row of straw beehives stood against the white picket fence in the rear, all ready for their summer occupants. William's wife was young and pretty. She was the girl with the dimples and the curls who had watched General George Washington march up Broad Way. William had thought that day she was the prettiest girl he had ever seen and he had married her soon afterward.

Her brother, James Paulding, a tall, slim young man, remembered Washington Irving and welcomed him, too.

"Now we are going to turn you loose," William told Washington the morning after his arrival. "You may take my fishing rod and my rifle and go anywhere you like."

"I'll pack you a lunch so you may stay all day," his pretty sister-in-law added.

126

Washington stood in the doorway and looked around him. What a perfect life it seemed to the lad! He had been kept at home for the better part of the winter because of ill health. Now he felt like a young bird trying out new wings. No mountain seemed too high for him to climb, no valley too deep for him to dip into. But he missed Tom Farley and Black Spot. They would have been perfect companions, and how they would have enjoyed it!

Washington felt very happy. After being ill most of the winter he suddenly seemed to be well and strong. He had never known such freedom. He whistled to William's dog, Wolf, and the animal bounded after him. Wolf wasn't so friendly as Black Spot, but he was nice enough.

"There's only one trouble with Wolf," William told his young brother. "He likes to get into fights with other dogs. Try to make him behave if you possibly can."

Washington trudged along the Albany Post Road, his brother's rod over his shoulder, the rifle tucked under his arm, the lunch in his pocket. He whistled gaily. He would have wonderful tales to tell Tom Farley when he got home.

Wolf ran on ahead. Robins chirped in the roadside bushes. Little white clouds, like a flock of baby lambs, scudded across the pale blue spring sky. The air smelled delicious.

Suddenly Washington was shaken from his happy mood by the sound of a dogfight. He ran toward it, remembering what William had told him. Wolf, he knew, was in trouble. He soon came upon Wolf and a white bulldog rolling together on the ground, snapping and snarling.

"Stop it, Wolf!" he shouted. "Stop, I say!" But Wolf paid no attention to him.

Then the door of a white house by the side of the road opened and a pretty girl, about eighteen, rushed out.

128

She carried a huge pepper pot in her hand and she was followed by a boy about Washington's age. She did not seem to be at all disturbed about the fighting dogs.

"Catch their collars while I shake this pepper into their eyes and noses!" she ordered. "They won't fight very long!"

She began to sprinkle the dogs as if they were something she had been cooking and was now seasoning. Then the dogs began to lose their enthusiasm for the fight.

The boys managed to pull the dogs apart. The owner of the white bulldog dragged him to the house and shut him in. Wolf knew he had done wrong. With his tail between his legs and a sheepish look on his face, he turned away.

"That's the last you'll see of him today," the girl said. "Come and sit down and have a drink of water from our spring. It's the coldest and the sweetest hereabouts."

Washington sat on a three-legged stool in the shade of the porch. The girl got a pitcher and went to the spring that bubbled up at the foot of a giant elm tree, and filled it. She returned with the pewter pitcher beaded with moisture and poured some into a gourd for Washington. "She is right," he thought. He had never tasted sweeter water.

"My name is Katrina Van Tassel," the girl said. She sat down and began to shell green peas into a yellow bowl. "And my brother's name is Harry. What's your name?"

"Washington Irving," he told her.

"Washington Irving. I like that. It goes well together." She said it again.

A young man came up the path. He was tall and handsome. Katrina blushed to the roots of her blond hair, and her slim fingers sent the peas rattling into the yellow bowl. She pretended she didn't see him.

"I stopped by to say I would be at your party tonight," he said.

Katrina looked up. She made a pretty gesture as though she were surprised. "How you startled me, Peter! I had no idea you were here."

"I said I'd be coming to your party tonight," Peter repeated.

Katrina tossed her head in its great white cap. "That will be nice," she said demurely. Then she added, "The schoolmaster is coming, too."

The young man scowled so that his handsome face grew quite ugly. "Why does he have to stick his long nose into everything?" he demanded and strode angrily away.

Katrina watched him until the garden gate swung shut behind him and he disappeared up the road. Then she laughed merrily. "What a wonderful time I am going to have tonight!" she said aloud, but to no one in particular.

Washington laughed, too. He thought that pretty Katrina and the handsome young man were like the hero and the heroine of a story. The schoolmaster with the long nose should play the part of the villain.

The Headless
Horseman

WASHINGTON IRVING and Harry Van Tassel liked
each other. Harry had the round face and blue
eyes of his Dutch ancestors. There was something about him that reminded Washington of
his friend Peter Gaansvoot. Harry had the same
placid manner, the same good nature. Washington was glad to have found a friend.

"I'll show you some good places to fish in the
Pocantico River," Harry offered.

Katrina packed him a lunch, too, and the boys
started off together.

"Do you believe in ghosts?" Harry asked as
they trudged along.

Harry spoke English differently from Washington. The Van Tassel family still used the Dutch language when they were at home. Katrina and Harry had learned to speak English only when they were old enough to attend the little log schoolhouse. There was a certain thickness in Harry's speech.

"I am not sure whether I believe in ghosts or not," Washington answered. "Why? Do you?"

"There are several here in Tarrytown," Harry said. "For instance, there's the ghost of the Hessian soldier, who lost his head in a skirmish near here. He rides the roads at night in search of his lost head. They say that sometimes he finds it. Then he carries it under his arm as he gallops back to the churchyard. He has to arrive there before the cocks crow. I've heard the sound of his galloping horse on the highway many nights. I pull the covers over my head and put my hands over my ears."

134

Washington shivered pleasurably. What would Tom Farley think of such a tale—Tom, who scoffed at ghosts?

"There's a rock near by called Kidd's Rock," Harry went on. "Captain Kidd is supposed to have buried treasure under it."

"My friend Tom Farley says bad luck comes on people who dig for buried treasure," Washington stated.

"Shucks! That's not true. I've dug many times. Bram Ten Brock and I keep our shovels hidden in the bushes near the rock, so we can dig at any time. We could try it this afternoon."

"Let's!" Washington cried. He had always wanted to dig for buried treasure.

After they had fished in the quiet pools of the small Pocantico River and strung their catch on a line, they tramped through the woods to Kidd's Rock. Washington could almost see the pirates in the shadows of the trees.

"The shadow from that beech tree has to fall a certain way," Harry explained. "I've never dug just at this time of day before. Maybe we'll find something."

The boys set to work quietly. A silence seemed to settle over the spring woods. Even the blue jays had stopped their scolding. The earth was moist from a recent rain, so it was easy to dig. Soon they had a wide, deep hole.

"How far do you suppose we should go?" Washington asked after a while. His back was getting tired and he had a row of blisters on the palm of each hand.

"Maybe five feet, maybe six," Harry answered.

"That's going to take us an awfully long time," Washington said. "We've dug about three feet now and I'm tired."

"A little deeper," Harry begged.

Five minutes later Washington's shovel struck something that gave forth a metallic sound.

"It's a chest full of gold! It's the lost treasure!" Washington shouted. "Hurry!"

They sent the dirt flying, forgetting their aching backs and sore hands.

Their shovels finally uncovered an old iron pot. It was a round black pot with squat legs that stuck up like three little horns.

"It's nothing but a nasty old cooking pot," Harry said and his speech grew even thicker with disappointment.

Washington bent over and picked it up. "It's been covering something!" he exclaimed. "Look! Aren't these beautiful!"

The old iron pot had been used to cover two silver tankards. They were black now with tarnish from being in the ground so long, but they were beautiful. The boys realized that.

"It's part of Captain Kidd's treasure!" Harry shouted, jumping up and down with excitement. "It is! I know it is!"

"Let's dig some more!" Washington cried. "Let's find the rest of the treasure!"

But, although they dug until sundown, that was all they found. By this time their hands were blistered and their backs ached.

"We'll take the tankards to the sheriff and ask him what to do with them," Harry said. He helped Washington shovel the dirt back into the deep hole they had made.

They followed the rough rambling road that was lined with elms and walnut trees and passed a few scattered Dutch cottages, set well back in gardens that would soon be blooming with hollyhocks and roses.

The sheriff was a wise and just man. He said he would take the tankards to the jeweler, have him polish them, and ask him to exhibit them in his shopwindow. If in thirty days no one stepped forward and proved he was the rightful owner, they should belong to the boys.

Hulda the Witch

WASHINGTON IRVING and Harry Van Tassel
vowed to be friends forever.

"You are my best friend next to Tom Farley,"
Washington said. Harry didn't mind that Tom
came first. He knew he was Washington's best
friend here in Tarrytown and this was all that
mattered. Harry had never had so much fun
with anyone else as he had with Washington.

Every day when the weather was good, they
explored the country near Tarrytown. Washington Irving was enchanted by this region. His
young imagination was stirred by the stories the
old people delighted to tell him.

He listened so closely that they felt flattered. The boy hung on every word they said. Best of all to the storytellers, he seemed to believe every word of their tales.

When he was not with Harry Van Tassel he was with James Paulding, the brother of William's wife. Although James was several years older than Washington they liked each other and enjoyed being together.

James Paulding was a great reader, too, and he lent Washington a number of books.

Washington soon made friends with James's grandfather. He was a stout old gentleman with twinkling blue eyes and a jolly smile. He had been born in Holland and still read his Dutch Bible, a great, thick book with silver corners and silver clasps.

Harry Van Tassel knew the best fishing places, but James Paulding took Washington hunting. Boys were taught at an early age to handle and care for their guns. William lent his gun to Washington whenever he wanted it.

There wasn't a hill or a dale within ten miles of the sleepy little town that Washington and his friend did not explore. Washington grew strong and rosy-cheeked. Probably neither Mr. John Jacob Astor nor the stout sister-in-law of Mrs. Kilmaster would have recognized him if they had met him again. He was no longer the pale slender lad of the stagecoach journey.

Washington and Harry dug again for treasure near Captain Kidd's Rock, but they never found anything more than the two tankards. They liked to walk past the window of the jewelry shop and stare at the tankards, which were shining and very beautiful now. So far no one had claimed them, so there was a good chance they would own them when the thirty days were up.

One afternoon after a good morning of fishing and a fine lunch eaten in the sweet-smelling spring woods, Harry said, "You've never seen the old Dutch church, have you, Washington?"

"No," Washington answered. "Let's go there." He was always ready for a new adventure and this sounded like one.

They walked along the Albany Post Road. There were deep ruts in it made by heavy rains and clumsy stagecoaches. They passed many rich farms. Towheaded children tumbled in the meadows and stood with round eyes to watch the boys as they went by. One house had an old felt hat nailed to a willow tree. Over its torn brim Washington caught a glimpse of half a dozen baby wrens waiting for their parents to come back with a dinner of worms for them.

The Dutch church stood on a knoll on the right-hand side of the road. The afternoon sun fell gently on its stone walls and tiny cupola. An old man sat on one of the overturned gravestones in the churchyard.

He was sunning himself and enjoying the warm April air as he smoked his pipe.

"Good afternoon," Harry said politely in his heavy Dutch voice. "This is my friend Washington Irving. He lives in New York City, but he is visiting his brother in Tarrytown. I brought him to see the grave of the headless Hessian soldier. May I show it to him?"

Old Ben, the sexton, took his clay pipe out of his mouth and nodded his white head.

"I'm glad to meet you, lad." Then he turned to Harry. "Don't forget to show him the grave of Hulda the Witch," he said.

"A witch!" Washington exclaimed excitedly. "A real witch? And buried in a churchyard?"

"You've a right to be surprised." Old Ben nodded. "Not many churchyards have one."

"Will you tell me about her?" Washington asked, seating himself on the new spring grass at the old man's feet.

For the next fifteen minutes he listened to the story of the foreign woman who had come to live in a small hut on the Sleepy Hollow road.

"We Dutch don't take to foreigners," old Ben told the boys. "We were suspicious of her from the start. Then we began to meet her on lonely roads at the full of the moon, a bag flung over her shoulder, a stick in her hand. Sometimes the children would report meeting her in the woods. They'd say she was digging up the queer herbs the Indians used for medicine. Sometimes the savages visited her, slipping like red shadows silently through the trees. People began to whisper that she was a witch. Later, when cattle started to grow sick and die, they were sure she had put spells on them. Feeling against her was strong. They wanted to run Hulda out of town."

"Did they?" Washington asked eagerly. The old man filled his pipe again. He lighted it and drew in deep comforting puffs.

Washington could scarcely wait for the sexton to go on. He could almost see the old woman with her bag and the Indians moving silently through the forest.

"Did they run her out of town?" the boy asked again, hoping to hear the rest of the story.

"No, because other and more important things happened. The war broke out and we heard that the British had sent a shipload of soldiers to land at the foot of the hill at Tarrytown. We men got together to protect our homes. We hid behind stone walls and trees along the road where the redcoats, as we called the English soldiers, would march. We told our women and children to lock the doors and bar the shutters and stay at home.

"The skirmish was bloody, for the soldiers were well trained and they outnumbered us two or three to one. We were getting the worst of it. Then Hulda the Witch appeared. She carried a musket and she took her place beside us.

146

"None of us had thought to send for her to stay with a family in a well-locked house. She lived alone in her hut by the side of the road, and in our trouble we had forgotten her. She took her place beside us men and fought better than a dozen of us. She turned the tide which was runing against us. But she was killed."

"I thought only a silver bullet could kill a witch," Washington said. "Did one of the British soldiers have a silver bullet in his gun?" Then he sighed. It seemed too bad that such a brave woman should have been killed. Yet she was a witch!

"No. Hulda was no witch. There aren't any witches, boys, any more than there are ghosts. She was a noble woman. We who had seen how brave she was were ashamed of what we had said about her and the way we had treated her. We were ashamed of the way we had forgotten her and left her alone in her little hut."

The old man spoke simply. "So we decided," he went on, "that she should be buried in the shadow of the church. There she lies, over there by the north wall." He motioned with his stubby pipe. "We have not forgotten her."

"That's the very best story of all," Washington said. He and Harry went to stand silently beside the grave of Hulda the Witch.

A Strange Cargo

HARRY CALLED for Washington very early one morning. Washington was still at the breakfast table, and Harry hopped from one foot to the other while he waited.

"Do you have to swallow the bowl, too?" he asked huffily as Washington scraped the bottom of his porridge bowl. "We'll be too late if you don't hurry. Do come on."

William's pretty wife laughed. "Don't hurry him, Harry! If you knew what a hard time I have had to work up that appetite in Washington! He pecked at his food like a bird when he first arrived."

"Now he gobbles it down like a——" Harry broke off before he said the word "pig." His Dutch politeness stopped his tongue in time. But the quick-witted Washington knew what he had meant to say and he laughed pleasantly.

"Come along!" he said, pushing back his chair and getting to his feet. "I've had enough. But why the hurry?"

"The 'Farmer's Daughter' docked an hour ago," Harry explained. His good nature was restored as soon as they were actually on their way. "I've got a message for my uncle, Gabriel Requa, who is the captain. Mother wants him to bring the things he bought for her and Katrina in New York when he comes to supper tonight. They're eager to see the new silks and cottons. Women are silly that way."

The two boys raced down the steep hill to the wooden wharf that jutted out into the shining water of the Hudson River.

The "Farmer's Daughter," a trim little white-painted boat, was tied up to it. A flimsy gang-plank led from the bank to her spotless deck.

At first the sailors wouldn't let the two boys on board. But they consented when Harry told them that the captain was his Uncle Gabriel.

Captain Requa was finishing breakfast in his cabin. He shouted a hearty welcome to the boys and bade them be seated. He tossed them a freshly baked loaf of bread from which he had just cut a generous hunk for himself.

"Help yourself!" he said hospitably.

Washington cut himself a slice and spread it with thick plum jam which the captain pushed toward him. Harry poured a mug of milk.

While Washington ate he looked around the captain's cabin. He thought it was the snuggest room he'd ever seen. There was a place for everything, and everything was in its place. He'd like such a room to live in forever.

There were shelves set into the wall above the captain's bunk. A hurricane lamp hung on a hook above the bunk.

"You like to read after you're in bed, don't you, sir?" Washington said. "So do I."

"That's the only time I have to read," the captain said heartily. "And at that I don't get enough reading to please me."

Washington nodded in sympathy. He knew how the captain felt. He, too, never seemed to have time enough to read all he wanted to.

"Washington Irving is going to write books when he grows up," Harry said proudly. "He can tell stories now better than anyone else I know. You should hear some of the tales he can tell about New York City. I think he knows everything that ever happened there. He's going to write a history about it someday. It must be a wonderful place. I never wanted to go there before, but now I do."

"So you are going to be a writer, young man?" The captain smiled. "What are you going to write about?"

Washington laughed. He was getting used to answering that question. Everyone asked it.

"First I'm going to travel around the world and write about what I've seen," he said.

Captain Requa nodded. "Good! I've been everywhere myself. I wish I had the ability to write down the things I've seen, but I haven't. Start your traveling in Spain. It is the most beautiful country in the world and I should know. Find your way to the old Moorish palace called the Alhambra. Here! I'll give you a present to remind you of what I've told you."

He got up, crossed the room and opened a big sea chest. In a moment he straightened up with a folded cloth in his hand. He brought it back to the table and laid it down carefully. Then he unwrapped a lovely blue tile.

"It's a bit chipped around the edges," he said, holding it out to Washington. "I picked it up in the courtyard of the Alhambra where a fountain plays all day long under an open sky. You must see the palace for yourself someday. Be sure to put down all you see carefully on paper, so that others who cannot travel may read and share the beauty of the place with you. When you do, remember me and this day and the tile I am giving you."

Harry had grown restless. He was a boy of action. He could sit still just so long, no longer. He got to his feet now. He moved toward the door. He delivered his mother's message. Washington wrapped the blue tile again and stuffed it in his pocket. The captain watched him.

"Ever plan to write about people?" he asked as Washington started to follow Harry.

"Oh, yes. I told President George Washington I would write about him," he answered.

Captain Requa tilted his head to one side like a sparrow. "I'll tell you someone to write about," he said. "Christopher Columbus! Ever thought of him? If it hadn't been for him and Queen Isabella of Spain, this country might not have been discovered. Ever think of that?"

"I'll go to Spain someday. I'll write about Columbus," Washington promised. His young head was full of dreams.

He followed Harry from the cabin. He stumbled along the passageway which was almost dark. He climbed the steep steps to the deck above. The brilliant sunshine blinded him.

Harry ran nimbly across the flimsy gangplank. Washington started to follow. But with his head full of dreams and his eyes full of sunshine he got confused and missed his footing!

With a terriffic splash he fell into the cold waters of the Hudson and sank from sight. Harry gave a squeal of fright.

For a minute Washington was numbed by the cold water and the shock. He splashed about helplessly. Harry saw his plight and dived in. A sailor rushed forward and tossed them a rope. Captain Requa, attracted by the commotion, came up in time to help haul the boys ashore.

Neither of them was the worse for his unexpected swim. They were strong, healthy lads and, as the captain said, a little water didn't hurt anybody.

A Voyage up the Hudson

Washington Irving was glad to be home. The bustling little city of New York seemed very lively after sleepy old Tarrytown.

Tom Farley had grown during Washington's absence. He was half a head taller now. But his friendship for Washington hadn't changed. He was still Washington's best friend.

Black Spot barked and raced around Washington, wild with delight to have him home again. Black Spot forgot that he was a middle-aged dog and acted like a puppy. Gussie was an old cat now. She spent most of her time sleeping in the sun or before the fire.

But she put herself out to welcome Washington home. She came to greet him, walking a little stiffly but still holding her thin black tail proudly aloft. Washington swooped her up in his arms and she purred contentedly.

Yes, it was good to be home. But when spring came again he was back in bed with one of his bad colds. This time his parents decided to send him north to visit his sisters Ann and Catherine. Mr. Irving went to see him off on his first trip up the Hudson River as far as Albany.

"I wonder if you'll like traveling by boat better than by stagecoach," Mr. Irving said as they stood together on the deck of the sloop.

"I'm sure I will," Washington answered, his eyes sparkling. "I've always wanted to go to sea, and this seems the next best thing."

"Mind you do what the captain tells you," Mr. Irving went on. "Remember he is in charge and is responsible for everyone on his boat."

Washington promised to obey rules and to do whatever the captain told him.

"Give Ann and Catherine my best love. Tell them we'll expect them for Christmas, as usual. We can't let the family drift apart, even if some of them have gone to live in the wilderness."

He chuckled at his own joke. He knew as well as Washington did that the little town of Johnstown, where Ann and Catherine had lived since they got married, was a gay little place. Both girls enjoyed a pleasant social life there. Like many people who live in a big city, Mr. Irving liked to pretend that he pitied anyone who didn't.

Washington was sorry to say good-by to his father, but he soon forgot him when the "Sea Gull" got under way. The captain and the crew of four Negroes were very busy until they had cast off and hoisted sail and were in the middle of the river, running swiftly before a strong wind.

159

Washington stayed on deck. He watched the captain and the crew and longed again to be a sailor. When things quieted down at last Washington went to stand beside the captain at the wheel. The high walls of the Palisades on the west side of the river reflected the early morning light. On top of them, where the woods were thick, wild birds made their home. Washington watched a flock of ducks fly over the water and disappear in the woods. The little city of New York was rapidly being left behind.

The captain kept the wheel until they were well outside the river traffic. Then he turned to Washington.

"Like to try your hand at steering?" he asked. He had a son about Washington's age and he liked boys. He was a "dark" Dutchman, with a long thin face, but his eyes were as blue as Harry Van Tassel's and his speech held the same soft Dutch thickness.

Washington could scarcely believe his luck. His hands trembled in excitement as he took the wheel. It was wonderful to feel that his hands could guide the ship wherever he pleased.

"We're making good time, but there's a storm brewing," the captain said after a while. He sniffed the air like a hound dog. "We'll probably run into it around Tappan Zee, where the river is so wide."

Black clouds were gathering in the west. A strong wind whipped at the sail. The ship strained under Washington's hands and turned into a wild creature he could no longer control. The captain took the wheel again.

What a storm it was! The lightning flashed. The thunder rolled. The waves were gigantic.

"The devil himself is stirring this brew," one of the colored sailors said, rolling his eyes.

" 'Tain't nothin' to be afraid of," another sailor spoke up.

161

He was an old man, with snow-white hair and faded brown eyes. He had sailed the river under the captain's father. He had seen worse storms.

"It's a day like this when you see the 'Storm Ship'!" another sailor whispered.

Washington scented a story. He forgot the storm for a moment. "The 'Storm Ship'? What's that?" he asked eagerly.

"Some say that Henry Hudson—may his soul rest in peace—still drives his ship, the 'Half-Moon,' across the length and breadth of Tappan Zee in a storm like this. That's the way he proves to timid sailors they will live through it," the captain explained. "Now get below, lad, and take that other boy with you. Stay in the cabin until I send word you can come out again."

Washington turned to look where the captain had pointed with the stem of his pipe. He hadn't noticed the tall, lanky, pale-faced boy who stood in the bow. He went to him at once.

162

"The captain says we are to go below and stay until he sends for us," Washington said pleasantly. "It's not safe for any of us to be here on deck for a while."

But the boy wasn't friendly. He looked Washington up and down, then turned away from him. "He can't boss me, nor you either. I'll stay up here as long as I like. I've paid my fare and I'm supposed to have the run of the whole boat. I can do as I like."

"But the captain is in charge and we should do what he tells us. . . ." Washington began.

But the rude boy said, "Oh, shut up! Go down to the cabin if you're a sissy and afraid of this little blow. I'm going to stay here. I don't want to be down with all those people, and I intend to see the storm, no matter what the captain says. I'm not afraid."

Washington left him. There didn't seem anything else to do.

164

He found the cabin crowded with men, women and children. It wasn't a very pleasant place to be, for some of them were sick and most of them were frightened. But the captain had told him to stay there, so he did.

The mother of the pale-faced boy was there. She was telling everyone that nobody could make her son come down to this stuffy cabin if he didn't want to.

"He knows his rights," she said proudly.

"But the captain is in charge and responsible for us all," Washington said.

"My son Dick thinks differently," said the silly woman and tossed her head.

Suddenly there was the sound of a great to-do on the deck above. The passengers huddled in the cabin heard someone cry, "Man overboard!" Several of the men rushed up on deck. Washington wanted to go, too, but he stayed where he was. He kept his promise to the captain.

165

One of the men returned and stuck his head in the cabin door. "It's your son Dick, ma'am," he said. "He's fallen overboard."

"He'll be drowned!" Dick's mother screamed and tried to rush out on deck, but many hands held her back.

"Yes, he may be drowned—and so may the two poor sailors who have gone to his rescue in a frail rowboat," the man in the doorway said. "And it's not their fault, as it is your foolish son's."

Dick's mother cried and cried. People tried to be kind and comfort her, but they couldn't help remembering how she had bragged that nobody could tell her son what he should do.

Suddenly they heard a great cheering.

"Your son has been saved!" someone shouted.

Then Dick's silly mother fainted.

The "Sea Gull" tied up at the dock in Kingston that night. Dick and his mother went ashore.

Washington was on deck early the next morning. He found a sunny spot and stretched himself out comfortably. He looked at the blue sky above him and the peaceful water of the river that lapped gently against the side of the boat. It didn't seem possible that there had been a storm the night before. And such a storm!

He stared up at the stern Catskill Mountains that raised their majestic heads into the clouds. He gazed with wonder at the cliffs, crowned with green forests. He watched eagles sailing and screaming around them. Nearby, in the river a big sturgeon leaped and fell back into the water.

The captain found him there and sat down beside him to smoke a pipe.

"That was a bit of nasty trouble we had yesterday," he said. "But all's well that ends well."

"I wished that I could help," Washington said.

"You helped by keeping your promise and staying in the cabin," he said.

Johnstown

"I DECLARE, you're getting handsome!" Washington's sister Catherine Paris said, giving him a welcoming kiss.

The stagecoach, in which he had rumbled up from Albany, had dropped its passengers at the Black Horse Tavern where his sister was waiting for him.

"Tell me," Catherine said affectionately, "have you outgrown your love for honey cake? I'll never forget that afternoon at Mr. Romaine's school and how you stood there chewing and chewing and swallowing and swallowing. I was sure you'd been struck dumb by stage fright!"

168

Then Catherine asked, "What happened to the red-haired girl you thought was so pretty?"

"Ann Trent?" Washington laughed. "Oh, she turned me down when I asked her to go to a party with me. She said I was too small."

"Well, she was as tall and thin as a bean pole!" Catherine said. "She must have been a head taller than you."

"I guess she was," Washington said good-naturedly. He knew now the old shoemaker had been right. He would never be a tall man.

"Ann and I have decided to divide your visit between us," Catherine said, when they reached her home. She led the way proudly into her bright little clapboard house. "Daniel will be home soon from work." Daniel Paris was her husband's name. "He too will be glad to see you. He says he'll show you better hunting and fishing than you had in Tarrytown. Oh, we hope you are going to be happy with us, Washington!"

He set out early the next morning to look over the small frontier town. It had a rough beauty of its own. The trees that lined the narrow street had once been kings in the forest. They towered high above the homes they sheltered. Secretly Washington preferred the sleepy charm of Tarrytown, still clinging to its slow Dutch ways. He made up his mind that he was going to live there someday. First he would see the world, and then he would settle down to write his books.

He followed the road out toward the large white manor house where Sir William Johnson had once lived. Washington knew the story of Sir William well. The brave and handsome Irishman had long been a hero to him. Many a time he had heard his father say that if Sir William had lived during the Revolutionary War, he would have prevented the Indian massacres.

Sir William Johnson had been the Indian agent in America, appointed by the English

King. While he lived the red men had loved and respected him and had been friendly.

Washington was so wrapped in his thoughts that he didn't notice the slight stirring of the bushes by the side of the road. He did not see the pair of bright black eyes that peered out at him. A moment later he stopped in his tracks, uttering a sharp exclamation of surprise. A tall, handsome Indian boy, about his own age, stood before him. He had just stepped silently from the thick underbrush.

Washington had not seen many Indians in his life, perhaps a dozen or more. Because he had just been thinking of their cruelty in the war, he was startled now to see one barring his path.

But the Indian boy held out a red-brown hand and smiled. "My name is Thundercloud," he said in good English. "I am a friend of your brother-in-law, Daniel Paris. He asked me to show you good places to hunt and fish."

"How did you find me?" Washington asked.

"I stopped at your house this morning, but you had already left. So I tracked you here."

"Tracked me?" Washington was interested. He had heard how clever Indians were in following people. "How?"

Thundercloud smiled, showing his strong white teeth. "Footsteps for one thing. The dust is thick, we need rain and you wear heavy-soled Dutch boots, which are easy to follow. Besides, you are a great kicker of stones. Starting outside the Paris' gate I found many stones you had kicked along the way."

The Indian's black eyes twinkled at the look of amazement on the white boy's face.

"You must teach me how to see so much," Washington said.

"I will." Thundercloud looked pleased. "Mr. Paris wants me to take you on an overnight fishing trip. He wants you to like it here."

"Oh, I'd like that!" Washington said.

They spent that morning at Sir William Johnson's house. No one lived there now but a caretaker. He was friendly and let the boys wander where they liked. He followed more slowly.

As they stepped across the threshold of the library where Sir William had died, the caretaker spoke softly. "Sir William was a great man," he said. "He was a good friend to the Indians, Thundercloud. He was talking to a council of your people, who had come from far and wide to hear him, when he was stricken by the sun that hot July day in 1774. I was a lad then, but I remember it well. They carried him into this room and here he died."

Later he showed the Indian boy and Washington Irving a row of hatchet marks on the mahogany railing of the staircase. They had been made by Sir William's brother-in-law, a great Indian chief.

"They were made to show the plundering Indians that they must leave this house alone and not burn it down," he explained. "The marks told them that this was the house of their friend, Sir William Johnson, and it must not be harmed."

Washington hated to leave the old place. His imagination peopled it with ladies and gentlemen in white-powdered wigs and gay satin clothes. Tall Indians in blankets and with war paint on their faces seemed to glide through the lower halls. The spirit of the great man, Sir William Johnson, seemed to be everywhere, filling the old place with friendliness and good cheer.

Canada Lake

Washington and Thundercloud made a long tramp from Johnstown with packs on their backs. Pleasantly tired, they arrived at Canada Lake at sundown the next day.

"We will make camp here," Thundercloud decided. The boys were on a point of land that jutted out into the blue waters of the lake. The Indian boy dropped his pack, wrapped in deerskin, on the ground.

The lads slept heavily that night. They awoke refreshed. The day was sweet with the scent of pine and balsam. Washington immediately ran to the lake for a swim.

The icy water felt good against his skin. He rolled over on his back and stared up at the cloudless sky. It was a day fit for a king. He had never felt so well. He kicked and splashed. He shouted with happiness. He just had to show his high spirits.

But he was ready to come out when Thundercloud called, "Breakfast!" He chewed on his piece of salt pork contentedly. It tasted much better, cooked out in the open this way, than it had when he and Black Spot were training to go to sea.

"This is a wonderful place," he said, looking around him. "How did you happen to find it, Thundercloud?"

"We came here every summer when my parents were alive," the Indian answered. "We camped above here on a piece of land that can be reached only by canoe. My people called this the Lake of Many Fishes."

The boys cleared up the remains of their breakfast. Then they made sure the fire was out and got their fishing poles and guns.

Thundercloud showed Washington where he kept a canoe hidden by the thick bushes on the lake shore. They paddled silently along the densely wooded bank. They let their fishing lines trail behind them. They looked about warily for game. These forests that swept northward to Canada were still the home of many wild animals.

Rounding a point of land they came upon a deer swimming in the water. It had somehow been hurt, for a trail of blood made the water behind it red.

Before Washington could take aim, the report of Thundercloud's gun echoed back and forth against the walls of mountains that surrounded the quiet lake. Thundercloud's bullet only wounded the deer.

The animal turned and tried to get back to shore. Washington hated to see it suffer. He took off his leather jacket and slipped his feet out of his stout Dutch boots. Then he sprang into the water and caught the wounded deer by the leg. The deer fought him off, but Washington caught him again, this time by the ear. With a few swift strokes Thundercloud beached the canoe and dived after the fighting animal.

The boys knew the deer was so badly hurt that if he got away from them he would die a slow and painful death in the forest. It would be kinder to kill him quickly. This Thundercloud did with his hunting knife. Then they dragged the body up on shore and sat down to get their breath before going any farther.

They took the dead deer back to their camp. Thundercloud showed Washington how to skin and divide it, so that they might take it home with them the next day.

After spending a perfect morning fishing, they sat down, under the shadow of a tall pine tree to eat their lunch. Then they went back to their fishing. The morning catch had been good, but neither boy had caught a bass as he had hoped. So they decided to cross the lake and try the other shore, which was rocky.

The fishing was excellent. In an hour Washington had three bass. Thundercloud caught two bass and a good-sized pickerel. A distant roll of thunder made them glance up quickly. They had been so intent on fishing they had not noticed that storm clouds had been banking in the west. Now the whole sky was black.

"We must get back to camp. Our things will be soaked if we don't get there in time to cover them," Thundercloud said.

They paddled furiously, but the west wind was strong. It seemed that for every foot they made forward they were pushed back two.

Lightning streaked the sky and thunder growled violently. The wind whipped the water into angry waves that threatened to swamp the light canoe at any moment.

"We'll never make it!" Washington groaned. His arms were tired from the difficult paddling and his back felt as if it were broken.

Thundercloud didn't answer. He just dug his paddle deeper into the rough water and pulled more strongly on it. Then Washington saw that Thundercloud wasn't making for their camping ground, after all, but for the long narrow island at the foot of the lake.

How grateful he was for the sound of pebbles scraping along the bottom of the canoe as they found a landing place on the rocky shore! They pulled up the canoe and turned it over. They got under it and kept as dry as they could while the storm raged. Washington soon began to enjoy the adventure again.

"Has this island a name?" Washington asked between claps of thunder.

The Indian boy nodded. "It is called Stoner's Island after a great white hunter and guide who used to come to this lake many years ago."

"Did he own it?" Washington asked.

Thundercloud shook his head. "No. But once when he had set his beaver traps along the shore of the lake, he came upon some Indians who had stolen the animals he had trapped. He accused them of it. They were three to one and wished to fight it out. He knew he would have no chance against them. So he ran and they gave chase. He jumped into the water and swam to this island and stayed here safely for two days and nights. He kept off the Indians until his friends came and saved him. Ever since it has been called Stoner's Island."

Washington admired the tale of the great hunter. "Is he still alive?" he asked.

"Yes. He lives not far from Johnstown. We'll visit him someday if you like."

Washington wanted very much to visit such a brave man. He thought Mr. Stoner would be able to tell some good tales of the Revolutionary War when he had acted as a guide.

The storm had died down and the boys paddled back to their camping ground.

Many Years Later

"Time passes quickly when you are in your twenties," Washington Irving said to Tom Farley when they met before the Federal Building at Wall and Broad Streets. Tom was still Washington's best friend after seventeen years.

"I want to hear about your trip to Europe and how you like studying law," Tom said. "Let's stop here at the Tontine Coffee House and talk."

Tom had made a long trip West with his father. Like John Jacob Astor, Tom's father was in the fur trading business. Tom told about his adventures and then said, "Why are you studying law? I thought you wanted to be a writer?"

Washington made a wry face. "I'd stop studying law tomorrow except for Matilda," he said. "I'm engaged to marry Matilda Hoffman, and I study law in her father's office. I'll practice law with Mr. Hoffman when I've passed my bar examinations. Then I can marry Matilda."

"Have you given up your writing?" Tom asked.

"I brought back stacks of notebooks scribbled full of what I saw in Europe," Washington said. "I traveled as Peter Gaansvoot said I should, with a dozen quill pens and plenty of paper. I'm going back, especially to Spain, and study Spanish history. But law and Matilda come first."

"What about your history of New York City? Nobody knew more about the city than you did."

"I'll let you into a secret, Tom. My brother Peter and I have made the beginning of a book we call Knickerbocker's History of New York. It might be done now if Peter hadn't left for Liverpool on business."

Dreams That Came True

Tom Farley and Harry Van Tassel, dressed in evening clothes, stood together in the parlor of Tom's house. They seemed to have turned back into the freckle-faced boys they used to be.

"Suppose Washington doesn't remember us!" Tom said for the twentieth time that evening.

"Don't talk nonsense!" Kathy, Tom's wife, said. "How could Washington Irving forget you two?"

"But Washington is well known now," Harry said in his slow Dutch voice. "He's become America's best-beloved author."

"And don't forget he's been the United States Ambassador to Spain," Tom broke in.

188

"I saw him twenty years ago, when he bought his home in Tarrytown," Harry said. "He named it Sunnyside. He went abroad soon afterward."

"He's known kings and queens, Kathy," Harry said. "Now all of New York is turning out to do him honor tonight."

"I hear that he is just as friendly and modest as he ever was," Kathy said stoutly.

"Washington and I met at the Tontine Coffee House many years ago," Tom said. "He told me he was studying law and was going to marry Matilda Hoffman. He also said he had begun to write *Knickerbocker's History of New York* with his brother Peter. I begged him to finish it."

"Poor Matilda died before their wedding could take place," Kathy said. "He finished the history after that. But he has never married."

"*Knickerbocker's History* made him famous," Harry said. "People like his stories of England, *Bracebridge Hall* and 'Newstead Abbey,' too."

"They helped to build up good will between the two nations, just as his *Legends of the Conquest of Spain* and his *Life and Voyages of Christopher Columbus* built up good will with Spain."

"My Uncle Gabriel Requa once gave him a blue tile from the courtyard of the old Moorish palace of Alhambra," Harry said. "Years later he wrote me that he had found the very place the tile had come from and had had it cemented back."

"Everywhere he went, and everyone he met turned into a book for him," said Tom. "When he was a boy he met John Jacob Astor. He wrote *Astoria* about Mr. Astor's wilderness town."

"My favorite is 'The Legend of Sleepy Hollow.'" Harry smiled. "Pretty Katrina was copied from my sister. Her lover is now my brother-in-law. The long-nosed schoolmaster looked very much like Ichabod Crane. I told Washington the legend of the Hessian horseman."

"Have you read 'Rip Van Winkle'?" Tom asked. "Washington told me the captain of the sloop 'Sea Gull' that carried him to Albany told him the legend of Henry Hudson's men. When the people of Catskill hear the thunder rolling through their hills, they say, 'There go Henry Hudson's men playing at bowls again!' He got that from the Dutch Captain."

"How Washington loved all those old Dutch stories about ghosts and witches!" Harry exclaimed. "They used to make chills run up and down his backbone. He even showed how nice people who were called witches could be."

"Washington always said Tarrytown was the happiest, sleepiest spot in the world," Tom said. "I was glad when he bought Sunnyside, his house there on the banks of the Hudson River."

"We hear he's going to stay there and write his story of George Washington," Harry said. "He's always tried to be worthy of his great name."

192

More About This Book

WHEN WASHINGTON IRVING LIVED

1783 WASHINGTON WAS BORN IN NEW YORK, NEW YORK, APRIL 3.

The estimated population of the thirteen colonies was 3,210,000.

The peace treaty with Great Britain was signed, ending the Revolutionary War, September 3.

1783– WASHINGTON GREW UP IN NEW YORK AND
1806 TRAVELED IN EUROPE FOR HIS HEALTH.

The Constitutional Convention met to frame the United States Constitution, 1787.

George Washington became the first President of the United States, 1789.

A banking system was established in the United States, 1791.

Eli Whitney invented the cotton gin, 1793.

Washington, D.C., became the capital of the United States, 1800.

The United States bought the Louisiana Territory from France, 1803.

1806– 1818	IRVING BECAME A LAWYER, ENTERED THE HARDWARE BUSINESS, AND BEGAN TO WRITE.

Robert Fulton built the "Clermont," the first practical steamboat, 1807.

The War of 1812 was fought, 1812-1815.

First account of the Lewis and Clark Expedition was published, 1814.

"The Star-Spangled Banner" was written, 1814.

1818– 1832	IRVING CONCENTRATED ON WRITING AND PRO- DUCED MANY BOOKS THAT MADE HIM FAMOUS.

Florida was purchased from Spain, 1819.

The Monroe Doctrine was issued, 1823.

The Erie Canal was completed, 1825.

Cyrus McCormick invented the reaper, 1831.

1832– 1859	IRVING LIVED ON AN ESTATE NEAR TARRYTOWN AND CONTINUED TO WRITE POPULAR BOOKS.

Samuel Morse invented the telegraph, 1835.

American settlers reached Oregon, 1836.

The Mexican War was fought, 1846-1848.

Gold was discovered in California, 1848.

California became a state, 1850.

The Lincoln-Douglas debates were held, 1858.

194

There were thirty-three states in the Union.

James Buchanan was President.

The population of the country was about 31,443,321.

DO YOU REMEMBER?

1. Where did the Irving family live when the story begins?

2. Where did Washington first go to school?

3. What did Washington do during the parade when George Washington was passing by?

4. What advice did President Washington give to Washington?

5. Why did Washington's father enroll him in a school run by Mr. Romaine?

6. Why did Mr. Romaine punish Washington with twenty lashes from a whip?

7. What did Washington do with the candy, cakes, and toys which he got for Christmas?

8. Where did Washington find the injured dog which he called Black Spot?

9. What happened when Washington took part in a play at school?

10. What interesting people did Washington meet on the stagecoach?

11. What story about a headless horseman did Harry Van Tassel tell Washington?

12. How did Washington and Harry Van Tassel recover some of Captain Kidd's treasure?

13. Who was Hulda the Witch?

14. What happened during Washington's trip up the Hudson River on a boat?

15. Who was Thundercloud, and what did he do to help entertain Washington at Albany?

16. What plans did Washington Irving have when he visited Tom Farley?

17. What books helped him to become famous?

IT'S FUN TO LOOK UP THESE THINGS

1. Where is The Netherlands, the home country of the Dutch in Europe?

2. Who first settled New York, and what was the settlement called?

196

3. When and for how long was New York the capital of the United States?

4. Where was George Washington inaugurated as the first President of our country?

5. How does New York rank in population among other large cities of our country?

6. What other famous American authors lived at the same time Washington Irving lived?

INTERESTING THINGS YOU CAN DO

1. Draw a map of Manhattan Island and show how it is surrounded by rivers.

2. Read to find out where the Battery is, which Washington Irving visited as a boy.

3. Find out how the Dutch obtained Manhattan Island from the Indians.

4. Collect pictures of early New York for an exhibit on the bulletin board.

5. Describe Rip Van Winkle or another interesting character from one of Irving's books.

6. Explain how an author prepares a manuscript in writing a book.

OTHER BOOKS YOU MAY ENJOY READING

Peter Stuyvesant, Mabel Cleland Widdemer. School and Trade Editions, Bobbs-Merrill.

Rip Van Winkle and the Legend of Sleepy Hollow, Washington Irving. Macmillan.

Silversmith of Old New York: Myer Myers, William Wise. Farrar.

Tales of Alhambra, Robert C. Goldston, retold from Washington Irving. Bobbs-Merrill.

Washington Irving, Catherine Owens Peare. Holt.

Wonder Tales of Seas and Ships, Frances Carpenter. Doubleday.

INTERESTING WORDS IN THIS BOOK

audience (ô'dĭ ĕns) : group of people assembled to hear a speaker

balcony (băl'kȯ nĭ) : platform projecting from the wall of a building

beeswax (bēz'wăks') : wax found in honeycomb

cobbler: person who makes and mends shoes

commotion (kȯ mō'shŭn) : noisy disturbance

conceited (kŏn sēt'ĕd) : vain, haughty

composition (kŏm′pȯ zĭsh′ŭn) : elements of writing, including selection of words and the formations of sentences and paragraphs

conscious (kŏn′shŭs) : knowing, mentally aware

delicious (dĕ lĭsh′ŭs) : pleasing to the taste

eerie (ē′rĭ) : ghostly, weird

enchant (ĕn chȧnt′) : charms, delude

engrossed (ĕn grōst′) : absorbed, fully occupied

enthusiasm (ĕn thū′zĭ ăs'm) : strong interest

excitement (ĕk sīt′mĕnt) : agitation, stirred up feelings

gable (gā′b'l) : triangular part of the wall of building, including the edges of the roof

gangplank (găng′plăngk′) : movable bridge-like platform used for boarding or leaving a ship

greedy (grēd′ĭ) : ravenous appetite for food and drink, also eagerness to own or possess

herb (ûrb) : plant used for medicine or for its sweet flavor

hoist: raise

imagination (ĭ măj′ĭ nā′shŭn) : formation of pictures in the mind of things not actually present in the surroundings

199

inhabitant (ĭn hăb′ĭt ănt) : person or animal that lives in a place

mahogany (mȧ hŏg′ȧ nĭ) : hard, dark, reddish-brown wood of a tree that grows in tropical America

marvelous (mär′vĕl ŭs) : wonderful

mascot (măs′kŏt) : person or thing supposed to bring good luck

mast (mȧst) : long, upright pole that supports the sails and rigging on a ship

miser (mī′zẽr) : person who lives poorly in order to save money

pewter (pū′tẽr) : mixture of copper and tin used in making dishes and other tableware

quavering (kwā′vẽr ĭng) : trembling, shaking

scone (skōn) : kind of tea cake, cooked on a griddle

sugarplum (shŏŏg′ẽr plŭm′) : candy made up in small balls or disks

suspicious (sŭs pĭsh′ŭs) : mistrustful

tankard (tăngk′ẽrd) : large vessel with a handle and lid

taper (tā′pẽr) : small wax candle

trundle bed (trŭn′d′l bĕd) : low bed that can be rolled under a higher bed

Childhood

OF FAMOUS AMERICANS

COLONIAL DAYS

JAMES OGLETHORPE, *Parks*
MYLES STANDISH, *Stevenson*
PETER STUYVESANT, *Widdemer*
POCAHONTAS, *Seymour*
SQUANTO, *Stevenson*
VIRGINIA DARE, *Stevenson*
WILLIAM BRADFORD, *Smith*
WILLIAM PENN, *Mason*

STRUGGLE for INDEPENDENCE

ANTHONY WAYNE, *Stevenson*
BEN FRANKLIN, *Stevenson*
BETSY ROSS, *Weil*
DAN MORGAN, *Bryant*
ETHAN ALLEN, *Winders*
FRANCIS MARION, *Steele*
GEORGE ROGERS CLARK, *Wilkie*
GEORGE WASHINGTON, *Stevenson*
ISRAEL PUTNAM, *Stevenson*
JOHN PAUL JONES, *Snow*
MARTHA WASHINGTON, *Wagoner*
MOLLY PITCHER, *Stevenson*
NATHAN HALE, *Stevenson*
NATHANAEL GREENE, *Peckham*
PATRICK HENRY, *Barton*
PAUL REVERE, *Stevenson*
TOM JEFFERSON, *Monsell*

EARLY NATIONAL GROWTH

ABIGAIL ADAMS, *Wagoner*
ALEC HAMILTON, *Higgins*
ANDY JACKSON, *Stevenson*
DAN WEBSTER, *Smith*
DEWITT CLINTON, *Widdemer*
DOLLY MADISON, *Monsell*
ELIAS HOWE, *Corcoran*
ELI WHITNEY, *Snow*
FRANCIS SCOTT KEY, *Stevenson*
HENRY CLAY, *Monsell*
JAMES FENIMORE COOPER, *Winders*
JAMES MONROE, *Widdemer*
JOHN AUDUBON, *Mason*
JOHN JACOB ASTOR, *Anderson*
JOHN MARSHALL, *Monsell*
JOHN QUINCY ADAMS, *Weil*
LUCRETIA MOTT, *Burnett*
MATTHEW CALBRAITH PERRY, *Scharbach*
NANCY HANKS, *Stevenson*
NOAH WEBSTER, *Higgins*
OLIVER HAZARD PERRY, *Long*
RACHAEL JACKSON, *Govan*
ROBERT FULTON, *Henry*
SAMUEL MORSE, *Snow*
SEQUOYAH, *Snow*
STEPHEN DECATUR, *Smith*
STEPHEN FOSTER, *Higgins*
WASHINGTON IRVING, *Widdemer*
ZACK TAYLOR, *Wilkie*

WESTWARD MOVEMENT

BRIGHAM YOUNG, *Jordan and Frisbee*
BUFFALO BILL, *Stevenson*
DANIEL BOONE, *Stevenson*
DAVY CROCKETT, *Parks*
JED SMITH, *Burt*
JESSIE FREMONT, *Wagoner*
JIM BOWIE, *Winders*